Table of Contents

Cluster Names

Literacy Plus

Robert J. Marzano
Diane E. Paynter
John S. Kendall
Debra Pickering
Lorraine Marzano

Word Book III

Zaner-Bloser, Inc.

Developed in cooperation with the
Mid-Continent Regional Educational Laboratory

Acknowledgements

McREL Staff

C.L. Hutchins, *executive director*
Jo Sue Whisler, *product development unit manager*
Shae Isaacs, *production manager*
Carol Meyer, *desktop publishing*
Jeanne Deak, *production assistant*

ISBN 0-88309-940-3

Zaner-Bloser, Inc., P.O. Box 16764, Columbus, Ohio 43216-6764

A Vocabulary Process Strategy

DECIDE  Decide that you want to learn a word.

FIGURE OUT  Try to figure out what the word means by:
    context clues
    word parts
    ask another person

VERIFY or FIND OUT Verify or find out the meaning by:
    dictionary/thesaurus/encyclopedia/glossary
    teacher/parent/expert
    cluster/similar words

MENTAL PICTURE  Create a mental picture:
    physical sensations/emotion/symbol
    see the word (spelled correctly)
    say the word

USE   Use or show you know:
    draw picture or symbol
    think of similar words
    create a sentence
    write a description in your own words
    list examples of the word

A

How to Add a Word

Is it in the index?

Yes	No

<table>
<tr><td colspan="3">MY WORD BOOK
Index</td></tr>
<tr><td>ideal</td><td>if…then</td><td>ill</td></tr>
<tr><td>identify</td><td>(igloo)</td><td>Illinois</td></tr>
<tr><td>idle</td><td>ignite</td><td>I'm</td></tr>
<tr><td>if only</td><td>ignorance</td><td>image</td></tr>
</table>

MY WORD BOOK

Index

ideal	if…then	Illinois
identify	ignite	I'm
idle	ignorance	image
if only	ill	imagination

1. Use the vocabulary process strategy.

1. Find a cluster where it might belong.

2. Write it where it fits.

3. Use the vocabulary process strategy.

Cluster Check List

	Conference Dates							
1. Occupations/Pursuits								
2. Types of Motion/Activity								
3. Size/Quantity/Weight								
4. Animals								
5. Feelings/Attitudes								
6. Food Types/Meal Types								
7. Time								
8. Machines/Engines/Tools								
9. Types of People								
10. Communication								
11. Transportation								
12. Mental Actions/Thinking								
13. Human Traits/Behavior								
14. Location/Direction								
15. Literature/Writing								
16. Water/Liquids								
17. Clothing								
18. Places Where People Might Live/Dwell								
19. Noises/Sounds								
20. Land/Terrain								

	Conference Dates							
21. Dwellings/Shelters								
22. Materials and Building								
23. The Human Body								
24. Vegetation								
25. Groups of Things								
26. Value/Correctness								
27. Similarity/Dissimilarity								
28. Money/Finance								
29. Soil/Metal/Rock								
30. Rooms/Furnishing/Parts of Dwellings/Buildings								
31. Attitudinals								
32. Shapes/Dimensions								
33. Destructive and Helpful Actions								
34. Sports/Recreation								
35. Language								
36. Ownership/Possession								
37. Disease/Health								
38. Light								
39. Causality								
40. Weather								
41. Cleanliness/Uncleanliness								

D

	Conference Dates								
42. Popularity/Familiarity									
43. Physical Traits of People									
44. Touching/Grabbing Actions									
45. Pronouns									
46. Contractions									
47. Entertainment/The Arts									
48. Walking/Running Actions									
49. Mathematics									
50. Auxiliary/Helping Verbs									
51. Events									
52. Temperature/Fire									
53. Images/Perceptions									
54. Life/Survival									
55. Conformity/Complexity									
56. Difficulty/Danger									
57. Texture/Durability									
58. Color									
59. Chemicals									
60. Facial Expressions/Actions									
61. Electricity/Particles of Matter									

E

1. Occupations/Pursuits

1A. Occupations (General)

workingman

employee

laborer

professional

breadwinner

craftsman

---

career

occupation

employment

livelihood

profession

role

sideline

---

chore

production

1B. Supervisors/Assistants

assistant

attendant

---

apprentice

---

landowner

manager

employer

foreman

landlady

landlord

landholder

---

director

chairman

chairperson

chairwoman

headmaster

headmistress

administrator

overseer

superintendent

supervisor

---

producer

sponsor

founder

1C. Royalty/Statesmen

congressman

congresswoman

senator

candidate

councilman

councilwoman

politician

delegate

tribune

---

ambassador

officeholder

official

dignitary

diplomat

statesman

duke

lord

duchess

earl

knight

monarch

sire

sultan

baron

czar

emperor

empress

nobleman

squire

vice president

figurehead

1D. Names of People in Sports

underdog

acrobat

athlete

diver

horseman

horsewoman

skater

swimmer

wrestler

daredevil

fighter

gymnast

skier

contestant

racer

ballplayer

baseman

batter

fielder

goalkeeper

shortstop

quarterback

halfback

umpire

lifesaver

referee

timekeeper

sharpshooter

archer

marksman

markswoman

1E. Reporters/Writers

announcer

weatherman

sportscaster

newscaster

newspaperman

poet

scribe

narrator

speaker

spokesman

spokesperson

spokeswoman

grower

picker

sharecropper

violinist

1F. Outdoor Professions

camper

fisher

fisherman

hunter

sportsman

sportswoman

trapper

digger

gravedigger

miner

stonecutter

rancher

cattleman

herdsman

ranger

roughrider

stockman

woodcutter

woodsman

forester

logger

lumberjack

lumberman

1G. Artists

designer

potter

architect

photographer

sculptor

conductor

drummer

musician

composer

soloist

soprano

1H. Entertainers/Performers

model

performer

comic

juggler

magician

fortuneteller

ventriloquist

mime

entertainer

showman

1I. Teachers/Students

principal

instructor

schoolmaster

schoolmistress

counselor

dean

tutor

adviser

freshman

graduate

sophomore

1J. Public Servants

inspector

patrolman

trooper

constable

sergeant

redcoat

airman

cavalryman

rifleman

colonel

corporal

1K. Areas of Work

agriculture

industry

military

politics

technology

1L. Scientists/Discoverers

engineer

vet

veterinarian

astronaut

mathematician

meteorologist

archeologist

astronomer

biologist

chemist

frogman

geographer

geologist

explorer

inventor

frontiersman

frontierswoman

discoverer

geography

astronomy

biology

chemistry

ecology

economics

geology

taxidermy

1M. People Who Buy and Sell

buyer

client

peddler

salesclerk

salesman

salesperson

saleswoman

shopkeeper

storekeeper

trader

agent

merchant

middleman

seller

tradesman

broker

vendor

1N. Small Business

blacksmith

clockmaker

goldsmith

locksmith

smith

watchmaker

brazier

cobbler

gunsmith

silversmith

cabinetmaker

coppersmith

bodyguard

barber

pastry cook

saloonkeeper

florist

dressmaker

weaver

miller

tailor

1O. People Who Work in Offices

businessman

businesswoman

secretary

typist

clerk

receptionist

1P. Builders

manufacturer

contractor

shipbuilding

1Q. Publishing

editor

printer

publisher

1R. People Who Clean Up

janitor

caretaker

custodian

1S. Occupations Related to Money

bookkeeper

accountant

cashier

teller

1T. Occupations Related to Imprisonment/Slavery

bondman

bondservant

gladiator

---

bondsman

slaveholder

hangman

warden

watchman

1U. Occupations Related to Medicine

dentist

physician

intern

psychiatrist

surgeon

1V. Occupations Related to Transportation

flier

skipper

copilot

---

shipowner

brakeman

seaman

shipmate

switchman

porter

stevedore

stewardess

1W. Clergy/Religious

missionary

nun

bishop

minister

pastor

pope

priest

prophet

abbot

apostle

clerical

deacon

hermit

monk

parson

rabbi

1X. Repairmen/ Construction Workers

mechanic

plumber

repairman

cameraman

surveyor

draftsman

draftsperson

technician

---

bricklayer

mason

stagehand

stonemason

1Y. Legal Participants and Occupations

attorney

1Z. Servants

butler

doorkeeper

doorman

housekeeper

servant

bellhop

gatekeeper

usher

chambermaid

chauffeur

coachman

handmaid

redcap

1a. Occupations Related to Restaurants

bartender

chef

busboy

1b. Messengers

messenger

operator

postmaster

news carrier

telegrapher

1c. Occupations Usually Held by Youth

nursemaid

1d. Work-related Actions

effort

labor

strive

toil

drudge

overwork

travail

employ

engage

layoff

retire

1e. Hobbies

collector

2. Types of Motion/Activity

2A. General Motion

activity

motion

movement

osmosis

kinetic

mobile

2B. Lack of Motion

motionless

standstill

static

inert

stagnant

stationary

dangle

hover

suspend

probation

suspension

await

hesitate

pause

postpone

procrastinate

putter

falter

lag

linger

interrupt

delay

waylay

defer

detain

hinder

interruption

lounge

2C. Beginning Motion

introduce

origin

source

genesis

introduction

initiation

preface

2D. The Act of Occurring

apply

function
commit

occur
undergo

react

reaction

2E. Completion
deadline

graduate
accomplish
fulfill

completion

deed

2F. Halting
cancel
quit
cease
halt
extinguish
lapse
terminate

prevent
obstruct
boycott
prohibit

obstacle

avoid
abstain

refrain

resist
restrain

smother
clog
congest
muffle
stifle

2G. General Actions Involving Coming/Going
arrival
oncoming

sightseeing
expedition
hitchhike
tour
exploration

migration

nomadic

depart
takeoff
withdraw

departure

dissolve
vanish

migrate
stray

approach
access

advance
proceed
headway
progress

2H. Pursuit

pursuit

pursue

2I. Taking/Giving

fetch
trundle
bear
import
shuttle

homecoming
retrieve

dispatch
export

relay
transfer

eliminate

furnish
supply

deposit
bestow

2J. Tossing/Catching Actions

cast
chuck
fling
flip

heave

flick

hurl

thrust

snag

2K. Pushing/Pulling Actions

insert

propel

inject

haul

tow

yank

lug

gravity

2L. Vibration

quiver

vibrate

shudder

throb

wobble

jitter

quake

totter

undulate

sputter

squirm

teeter

waver

vibration

juggle

scramble

jumble

2M. Shifting Motion

fishtail

shift

skid

slip

sway

2N. Jerking Motion

budge

bob

fidget

lurch

twitch

flounce

jolt

deflect

jounce

2O. Ascending Motion

rank

rate

hoist

pry

elevate

mount

rise

skyrocket

arise

ascend

ascent

2P. Descending Motion (General)

tumble

collapse

descend

landslide

plunge

topple

descent

tilt

dunk

dip

sag

droop

slump

slouch

2Q. Descending Motion Done by Human Beings

crouch

squat

stoop

sprawl

2R. Reduction

diminish

dwindle

wither

shrivel

letup

wilt

contraction

compression

reduce

condense

compress

cramp

corrugate

crumble

crumple

crinkle

2S. Expansion

explosion

expansion

enlarge

magnify

swell

expand

protrude

bulge

jut

blast

erupt

explode

discharge

2T. Force

pressure

inertia

propulsion

2U. Closing/Opening Actions

ajar

2V. Joining Actions

connection

seam

bond

hookup

attach

federate

splice

accompany

combine

connect

link ...

unite

associate

engage

fuse

graft

merge

synthesis

union

wedding

marriage

consist

constitute

contain

include

involve

comprise

intersect

collide

pinwheel

twirl

whirl

rotate

revolve

fasten

hitch

tether

affix

shackle

clockwise

counterclockwise

orbital

2W. Separating Actions

disconnect

divorce

detach

bisect

invert

reverse

reciprocal

unwind

swerve

swivel

2X. Circular/Angular Motions

circulation

rotation

surround

enclose

encircle

3. Size/Quantity/Weight

3A. Size/Weight

greatness

measurement

bulk

wee

lightweight

miniature

compact

stubby

petite

enormous

jumbo

mammoth

vast

immense

massive

monstrous

3B. Measurement Actions

fathom

3C. Measurement Devices

compass

gauge

protractor

speedometer

3D. Things Commonly Measured

latitude

longitude

angle

circumference

diameter

radius

meridian

census

3E. Specific Units of Measurement

centimeter

kilometer

mil

volt

watt

gram

kilogram

ounce

metric

degree

bushel

handful
mouthful
pinch

3F. Partitives

fluff
speck
powder
speckle
gob
particle

version

factor
fragment

module
portion
segment
species
subset

crumb
slab
splinter
sawdust
scrap
sliver
morsel

category

3G. General Amounts

volume
capacity
quantity

entire

countless
abundant
extensive
unlimited
numerous

abundance

ample
lush

leftover
excess
stub
surplus

exceed

outnumber	sole	threescore
additional	partial fractional	decimal data integer numeration
increase		
	lack shortage	**3I. Specifiers**
decrease deduct		either
	plural singular	
majority		**3J. Diminishers**
		broadly general(ly) roughly approximate(ly) overall
	3H. Cardinal/Ordinal Numbers	
couple binary mate	billion trillion	
	fourscore trice triple	particularly simply in particular
particular		

17

purely

insofar

largely

more or less

adequate

mild(ly)

partly

somewhat

slightly

at least

mere(ly)

piecemeal

in the least bit

barely

in the slightest

scarcely

practically

as good as

probable

3K. Intensifiers

complete(ly)

fully

perfectly

downright

entire(ly)

thorough(ly)

totally

widely

absolute(ly)

extreme(ly)

utmost

utter(ly)

greatly

terribly

a great deal

by far

intense(ly)

notably

4. Animals

4A. Animals (General)

mascot

livestock

amphibian

invertebrate

aquatic

4B. Cats/Dogs

cougar

tomcat

wildcat

lioness

panther

puma

bobcat

puss

coyote

dingo

hyena

jackal

beagle

bulldog

collie

foxhound

greyhound

mutt

poodle

spaniel

terrier

bloodhound

pug

wolfhound

4C. Reptiles/Mythical Animals

rattlesnake

serpent

mermaid

unicorn

nymph

4D. Baby Animals

fawn

yearling

dogie

4E. Land Animals (General)

antelope

elk

doe

gazelle

stag

stallion

bronco

horseflesh

jackass

mare

mustang

pinto

racehorse

stud

steed

bull

bison

llama

bighorn

ram

hog

sow

anteater

opossum

platypus

yak

camel

raccoon

weasel

badger

cottontail

hare

hedgehog

mink

mole

polecat

4F. Rodents

porcupine

woodchuck

muskrat

rodent

shrew

4G. Primates

gorilla

4H. Sea Animals

porpoise

walrus

dolphin

humpback

swordfish

shark

hammerhead

cod

guppy

salmon

seahorse

minnow

bass

carp

codfish

flounder

herring

smelt

snapper

sunfish

trout

tuna

4I. Shellfish and Others

jellyfish

sponge

eel

stingray

lobster

crayfish

mollusk

cockle

oyster

scallop

snail

octopus

squid

4J. Birds

blackbird

blue jay

bluebird

canary

cuckoo

dove

finch

lark

oriole

ostrich

sparrow

turtledove

vulture

hummingbird

meadowlark

mockingbird

parakeet

raven

songbird

wren

skylark

starling

gander

pheasant

cock

quail

swan

crane

drake

mallard

waterfowl

albatross

4K. Insects

flea

grasshopper

housefly

wasp

yellow jacket

dragonfly

hornet

drone

firefly

gnat

centipede

glowworm

slug

termite

cockroach

mite

silkworm

millipede

mantis

parasite

flatworm

4L. Parts of Animals

cowhide

hide

pelt

doeskin

rawhide

mane

bristle

fleece

plume

quill

snout

fin

flipper

hoof

talon

antenna

antler

ivory

tusk

whalebone

pouch

cud

gill

sac

4M. Animal Dwellings

aquarium

coop

henhouse

pigsty

stall

stockyard

lair

roost

honeycomb

beeswax

4N. Animal Equipment

rein

bridle

chaps

halter

harness

leash

muzzle

stirrup

saddlebag	horseless	
4O. Actions related to Animals		
sting swarm swoop		
graze		
gallop buck stampede		
snare		
horseback bareback		

23

5. Feelings/Attitudes

5A. Names for Feelings (General)

mood

impulse

sensation

emotion

impression

5B. Fear

horror

panic

fright

frightful

bloodcurdling

eerie

cautious

frantic

5C. Actions Associated with Fear

startle

terrify

cringe

haunt

horrify

flinch

petrify

5D. Worry/Guilt

shame

embarrassment

guilt

guilty

fret

strain

concern

anxiety

suspense

tension

uncomfortable

uneasy

tense

5E. Anger

rage

temper

fury

huff

revenge

wrath

bitterness

hatred

scorn

contempt

resent

despise

displease

irritate

offend

disgust

incense

outrage

furious

hostile

warlike

5F. Meanness/Cruelty

meanness

cruelty

merciless

vicious

destructive

savage

violent

drastic

ferocious

5G. Irritability

disagreeable

bad tempered

gruff

irritable

scornful

saucy

impertinent

5H. Sadness

gloom

letdown

discomfort

heartache

heartbreak

sorrow

dismay

doldrums

loneliness

misery

remorse

woe

contrite

downhearted

forlorn

sorrowful

wretched

grief-stricken

heartsick

pitiful

regret

suffer

grieve

mourn

sulk

repent

5I. General Upset

disappoint

	5J. Excitement	5K. Fun/Joy
discourage	astonishment	glee
frustrate	hubbub	mirth
depress	awe	
balk	amazement	
deject	disbelief	
disrupt	ecstasy	enjoyable
impose	passion	carefree
infringe		jubilant
interfere		rollicking
molest		
	amaze	
	astonish	
earnest	appall	pamper
solemn	marvel	
somber		
dour		
sullen		frolic
	thunderstruck	
distress		riddle
discontent	thrill	gag
	tingle	jest
	rejoice	antic
	arouse	wisecrack
dissatisfied		

5L. Comfort/Contentment

contentment

pity

sympathy

tame

civilize

soothe

console

sympathize

peaceful

snug

undisturbed

mellow

5M. Jealousy/Envy

jealousy

envy

grudge

jealous

possessive

5N. Hope/Doubt

belief

faith

desperate

hopeless

disappointment

doubt

despair

desperation

5O. Caring/Trusting

admire

appreciate

favor

prefer

regard

fond

adore

romance

appreciation

affection

gratitude

admiration

mania

depend

rely

support

entrust

pardon

5P. Neglecting Actions	5R. Human Traits (General)	
omit	ability	
overlook	talent	
neglect	capacity	
	flair	
	knack	
exclude		
isolate		
	discipline	
	personality	
	bearing	
5Q. Desire		
expect		
seek	characteristic	
anticipate	quality	
crave	attribute	
hanker	trait	
yearn		
greed		
5P. Neglecting Actions	**5R. Human Traits (General)**	

6. Food Types/Meal Types

6A. Types of Meals

buffet

chow

refreshment

banquet

6B. Food Types

nutrition

hash

nourishment

diet

supplies

seafood

relish

garnish

legume

pulp

calorie

carbohydrate

cellulose

protein

glucose

6C. Sweets

marmalade

molasses

popover

pastry

tart

shortcake

wafer

caramel

gumdrop

sherbet

lozenge

patty

taffy

toffee

bonbon

cocoa

licorice

peppermint

butterscotch

spearmint

vanilla

6D. Prepared Foods

macaroni

noodles

spaghetti

porridge

gruel

loaves

muffin

biscuit

cornbread

flapjack

johnnycake

tortilla

watercress

6E. Meats

poultry

steak

beefsteak

bologna

lard

mutton

pemmican

pork

6F. Dairy Products

curd

6G. Ingredients Used to Prepare Foods

cornmeal

gelatin

starch

sugarcane

cornstarch

mustard

spice

cinnamon

garlic

cloves

ginger

herb

nutmeg

parsley

catsup

vinegar

mayonnaise

6H. Things to Drink

buttermilk

coffee

cider

nectar

beverage

beer

alcohol

wine

champagne

gin

liquor

whiskey

broth

chowder

6I. Fruits

apricot

applesauce

plum
fig
prune

lime
tangerine

pineapple
coconut

melon
honeydew

6J. Vegetables

beet

cabbage

pickle

spinach

turnip

eggplant

yam

squash

corncob

oats

soybean

maize

malt

barley

bran

rye

acorn

chestnut

kernel

almond

cashew

nutshell

pecan

walnut

6K. Actions Done to/with Food

brew

grill

broil

poach

scald

simmer

skewer

sift

knead

rot

decay

deteriorate

31

6L. Food Tastes

flavor

tang

savor

---

sweetness

bitterness

---

succulent

---

rotten

stale

6M. Eating/Drinking Actions

gnaw

munch

nibble

---

dine

devour

---

gorge

sup

consume

---

gargle

guzzle

6N. Hunger/Thirst

appetite

7. Time

7A. Time (General)

lifetime

mealtime

peacetime

wartime

7B. Devices Used to Measure Time

calendar

stopwatch

wristwatch

hourglass

sundial

timepiece

date

7C. Parts of a Day

dawn

noonday

daybreak

sunup

workday

midday

midnight

overnight

sunset

dusk

nightfall

sundown

twilight

instant

7D. Other Periods of Time

cycle

lifelong

meantime

term

countdown

duration

generation

interval

yule

century

decade

7E. Months and Days

January

7F. Relative Time

future

eternity

morrow

bygone

relic		introductory
boyhood childhood youth	**7G. Prior Action (Relationship Markers)** lately prior to	
		brandnew current recent
	former previous	
ancient antique secondhand		due
	as yet at first before now before that in the beginning so far until then up to now beforehand heretofore hitherto	now that
colonial prehistoric historic historical primitive medieval		**7H. Subsequent Action (Relationship Markers)** eventually momentarily
history ancestry	original source initial	afterwards henceforth henceforward latter thereafter

hereafter

hereinafter

subsequently

tardy

eventual

7I. Concurrent Action (Relationship Markers)

at this point

immediately

nowadays

presently

thereof

whilst

at the same time

in the meantime

meanwhile

simultaneously

7J. Speed

pace

tempo

velocity

bustle

fuss

haste

flurry

frenzy

scoot

accelerate

hasten

hustle

scurry

whisk

brisk

rapid

swift

jiffy

fleet

presto

brief

immediate

instant

automatic

abrupt

prompt

spontaneous

hastily

automatically

offhand

headfirst

helter-skelter

hasty

headlong

7K. Duration/Frequency

constant

endless

everlasting

permanent

continuous

eternal

---

occasional

temporary

infrequent

irregular

momentary

---

longtime

longstanding

---

forevermore

---

seldom

---

nevermore

---

persist

---

repeat

rehearse

---

annual

general

usual

customary

frequent

continual

8. Machines/Engines/Tools

8A. Machines

hardware

machinery

appliance

apparatus

equip

mechanical

clockwork

mechanism

contraption

gadget

rig

8B. Engines and Parts of Engines

brake

gear

starter

generator

compressor

crankshaft

piston

throttle

turbine

8C. Fuels/Lubricants

petroleum

diesel

turpentine

refuel

grease

lubricate

tallow

8D. Appliances

cook stove

griddle

burner

furnace

boiler

kiln

radiator

freezer

icebox

phonograph

stereo

8E. Tools (General)

aid

device

implement

utensil

drill

screwdriver

pliers

wrench

crowbar

jack

lever

wedge

sledge

hoe

pitchfork

spade

chisel

sandpaper

scraper

8F. Tools Used for Cutting

ax

axe

hatchet

scythe

sickle

jackknife

pocketknife

razor

lawnmower

trimmer

blade

barb

8G. Cutting/Abrasive Actions

peck

pierce

prick

stab

grate

chafe

whittle

grind

shred

slash

gnash

hack

mince

slice

snip

cutoff

shear

slit

crosscut

pare

---

burrow

scoop

bulldoze

dredge

excavate

8H. Fasteners

fishhook

hinge

latch

screw

spike

brad

peg

slot

rivet

---

clamp

clothespin

---

staple

tack

thumbtack

---

cable

clothesline

cord

fishline

lariat

thong

twine

drawstring

---

handcuff

keyhole

bolt

8I. Handles

grip

---

knob

hilt

8J. Miscellaneous Devices

dial

trigger

toggle

---

windlass

---

pulley

spool

spindle

---

platform

stepladder

easel

springboard

sawhorse

baton

pointer

wand

8K. Equipment Related to Vision

telescope

binoculars

eyepiece

spyglass

lens

8L. Electronic Equipment

transistor

terminal

thermostat

8M. Utensils Used for Cooking/Eating

silverware

tablespoon

tableware

chopsticks

kettle

saucepan

skillet

crock

stewpan

dipper

ladle

spatula

tong

sieve

nutcracker

opener

mug

glassware

water glass

goblet

stein

casserole

china

platter

chinaware

kitchenware

8N. Weapons

firearms

weapon

arms

harpoon

spear

tomahawk

cutlass

dagger

javelin

lance	explosive	
pistol rifle cannon revolver shotgun musket	arrowhead dart boomerang sling slingshot bowstring crossbow	
bomb bombshell bullet gunshot ammunition cannonball missile pellet torpedo dynamite grenade gunpowder	guillotine noose	

9. Types of People

9A. People (General Names)

chap

character

individual

folk

mankind

highness

majesty

9B. Names for Women

squaw

widow

belle

dame

feminine

gentlewoman

ma'am

mistress

spinster

hostess

madam

madame

lass

schoolgirl

tomboy

maiden

9C. Names for Men

gentleman

gentlemen

guy

master

mister

señor

masculine

dude

bachelor

host

schoolfellow

junior

urchin

9D. Names Indicating Age

newborn

papoose

toddler

infant

tot

embryo

kid

minor

juvenile

orphan

youngster

teen

senior

elder

9E. Names Indicating Friendship/Camaraderie

buddy

classmate

partner

playmate

roommate

schoolmate

teammate

chum

peer

playfellow

acquaintance

ally

boyfriend

girlfriend

darling

lover

suitor

fiance

mate

sweetheart

9F. Names for Spiritual or Mythological Characters

pixy

sandman

genie

spook

saint

soul

goblin

demon

imp

phantom

crossbones

ghoul

wizard

hag

9G. Names Indicating Negative Characteristics about People

gossip

liar

storyteller

telltale

busybody

coward

dunce

blockhead

dolt

dope

delinquent

moron

nuisance

scatterbrain

bully

attacker

brute

cad

foe

opponent

rascal

rival

scamp

hothead

ruffian

scoundrel

---

suspect

hunchback

prey

victim

captive

castaway

hostage

invalid

---

wallflower

---

crook

gunfighter

rustler

cannibal

convict

jailbird

outlaw

vandal

criminal

lawbreaker

pickpocket

tyrant

villain

wrongdoer

9H. Names Indicating Lack of Permanence for People

tourist

vacationer

---

gypsy

hobo

runaway

wanderer

fugitive

rover

vagabond

---

passenger

spectator

9I. Names Indicating Permanence for People

settler

colonist

newcomer

puritan

townsman

---

townsfolk

villager

dweller

townspeople

inhabitant

tenant

tribesman

---

citizen

native

aborigine

---

foreigner

alien

countryman

countrywoman

taxpayer

traitor

veteran

9J. Names Indicating Size of People

runt

pygmy

9K. Names Indicating Fame

savior

celebrity

heroine

idol

9L. Names Indicating Knowledge of a Topic

ace

expert

genius

pro

scholar

gamesman

veteran

virgin

rookie

amateur

novice

9M. Names Indicating Financial Status

peasant

millionaire

9N. Family Relationships

household

relative

ancestor

heir

descendant

offspring

pedigree

godfather

patriarch

guardian

godmother

sissy

godchild

goddaughter

godson

bride

groom

bridegroom

bridesmaid

grandnephew

cousin

9O. Names Indicating Political Disposition

confederate

democratic

republican

10. Communication

10A. Communication (General)

comment

remark

declaration

exclamation

expression

proclamation

testimony

proposal

---

communicate

discuss

chat

converse

negotiate

brainstorm

---

conversation

discussion

powwow

dialogue

---

sermon

lecture

---

talkative

eloquent

vocal

---

jabber

drawl

blab

10B. Communication Involving Confrontation or Negative Information

challenge

disagree

debate

gripe

squabble

---

decline

rebel

revolt

defy

reject

oppose

---

betray

exaggerate

con

deceive

distort

---

swear

curse

damn

profane

---

argument

complaint

quarrel

spat
criticism
dispute
objection
trial

threaten
menace

threat

accuse
criticize
nag
condemn
denounce
sue

embarrass
mock
insult
ridicule

scoff
jeer
slur

disgrace

foolishness
deceit
exaggeration
falsehood
rumor
hearsay
hyperbole

10C. Communication Involving General Presentation of Information

exhibit
present
demonstrate
inform
notify
acquaint

refer
convey
indicate
specify

telegraph
broadcast
transmit

brag
express
preach
advertise
claim
declare
utter

accent
emphasize
stress

10D. Communication Involving Positive Information

cooperate

participate

teamwork

awe

charm

soothe

assure

encourage

flatter

inspire

compliment

congratulate

acknowledge

congratulations

worship

tribute

10E. Persuasion

convince

influence

sway

bait

tempt

bias

bribe

lure

persuade

plead

coax

urge

appeal

petition

suggest

advise

cue

recommend

hint

10F. Questions

respond

comeback

retort

bid

poll

beckon

propose

request

examination	permit	authority
	license	leadership
consult	yield	deny
inquire	conform	forbid
interview	consent	revoke
confer	submit	ban
		repeal

10G. Communication Involving Supervision/Commands

	control	

10H. Giving Out Information Previously Withheld

instruction	manage	expose
suggestion	administer	reveal
counsel	govern	
guideline	reign	
	preside	
	regulate	
	supervise	admit
		apologize
		confess
		confide
insist		
demand		
require	compel	
decree	enforce	
summon		

10I. Promises

		vow
•		guaranty

plea

pledge

10J. Recording or Translating Information

recording

quotation

translation

interpret

translate

quote

10K. Exclamations (General)

aw

ole

ooh

ugh

ay

bravo

gee

alas

aye

farewell

howdy

51

11. Transportation

11A. Types of Transportation

auto

rattletrap

vehicle

motorcar

jalopy

---

pickup

sedan

---

subway

streetcar

trolley

---

scooter

tricycle

unicycle

caboose

locomotive

---

carriage

chariot

stagecoach

hayrack

horsecar

11B. Work-related Vehicles

barrow

steamshovel

forklift

reaper

derrick

---

conveyor

11C. Vehicles Used in Snow

bobsled

11D. Vehicles Used for Air Transportation

airline

airliner

aircraft

seaplane

---

airship

glider

blimp

11E. Vehicles Used for Sea Transportation

ark

vessel

whaleboat

icebreaker

ferry

flatboat

liner

barge

ferryboat

freighter

tanker

battleship

carrier

sub

submarine

warship

flagship

showboat

steamboat

steamer

steamship

tugboat

dinghy

sailboat

yacht

cutter

schooner

raft

kayak

rowboat

shipwreck

11F. Parts of Vehicles

anchor

buoy

gangplank

mast

mainstay

porthole

rudder

gunwale

helm

outboard

prow

oar

axle

hub

headlight

windshield

parachute

propeller

53

cockpit

rotor

wingspread

11G. Actions and Characteristics of Vehicles

launch

cruise

navigate

marine

naval

aerial

airborne

passenger

cabdriver

stowaway

transport

aviation

11H. Things Traveled On

freeway

parkway

roadway

boulevard

byway

causeway

highroad

racetrack

speedway

racecourse

intersection

crossroad

detour

passageway

route

shortcut

wayside

roadside

drawbridge

span

rail

railway

sidetrack

ramp

chute

archway

waterway

airway

seaway

airfield

airstrip

runway

12. Mental Actions/Thinking

12A. Thought/Memory (General)

imagination

memory

reflection

conscience

concentrate

memorize

consider

meditate

ponder

reckon

recall

recollect

amnesia

12B. Subjects/Topics

core

subject

topic

theme

essence

keynote

objective

scheme

strategy

viewpoint

layout

scope

12C. Mental Exploration

examination

inspection

investigation

experimentation

inspect

research

analyze

investigate

probe

review

survey

rummage

schoolwork

12D. Mental Actions Involving Conclusions

compose

create

invent

intend

devise

improvise

solve

calculate

compute

conclude

determine

abstract

derive

infer

confirm

resolve

hunch

theory

prediction

suspicion

estimate

suppose

assume

forecast

revise

suspect

conjecture

foresee

predict

speculate

evidence

invention

proof

principle

solution

calculation

indication

indicator

enigma

12E. Consciousness

conscious

unconscious

nightmare

vision

fantasy

trance

daze

doze

snooze

hypnosis

stupor

waken

rouse

daydream

fantasize

57

12F. Interest

intrigue

concentration

curiosity

12G. Teaching/Learning

instruction

suggestion

educate

instruct

realize

glean

decoy

outsmart

outwit

complicate

confuse

confound

mystify

comprehend

breakthrough

lore

12H. Processes and Procedures

process

recipe

routine

tactics

logic

procedure

technique

12I. Definition

definition

define

represent

interpret

symbolize

12J. Choice

weed

discriminate

judgement

verdict

misjudge

assign

appoint

dedicate

12K. Intelligence

ignorance

intelligence

stupidity

intellect

wit

brilliant

intelligent

shrewd

ignorant

uneducated

unskilled

crude

naâve

vulgar

scientific

practical

intelligible

logical

rational

capable

skillful

competent

adept

deft

creative

imaginative

12L. Beliefs

ideal

superstition

creed

doctrine

mythology

philosophy

custom

instinct

tradition

vice

13. Human Traits/Behavior

13A. Kindness/Goodness

charity

mercy

---

courtesy

grace

consideration

hospitality

---

sensitive

sympathetic

liberal

clement

---

grateful

---

kindhearted

social

---

affectionate

attentive

---

generous

unselfish

willing

---

courteous

gracious

respectful

civil

noble

tactful

13B. Eagerness/ Dependability

sincerity

dependability

reliability

trustworthiness

---

eagerness

enthusiasm

ambition

determination

spirit

---

service

duty

responsibility

---

efficient

productive

diligent

effective

industrious

thorough

---

dependable

responsible

earnest

reliable

sincere

trustworthy

---

depend

rely

---

active

lively

enthusiastic

ambitious

animated

energetic

vigorous

---

pep

vigor

zest

13C. Lack of Initiative

idle

easygoing

dormant

inactive

lax

listless

casual

aimless

13D. Freedom/ Independence

freedom

liberty

independence

---

independent

voluntary

---

imprison

---

dependent

obedient

13E. Confidence/Pride

hopeful

confident

frank

---

confidence

pride

conceit

smug

vain

haughty

13F. Patience

expectant

impatient

patient

restless

patience

13G. Luck/Probability

fortunate

successful

prosperous

unfortunate

13H. Strictness/Stubbornness

headstrong

ornery

steadfast

stubborn

obstinate

resolute

rigor

sober

stuffy

grave

strict

severe

stern

13I. Humor

humorous

hilarious

witty

wry

13J. Spirituality

holy

religious

sacred

spiritual

divine

heathen

artistic

13K. Prudence

sensible

chaste

discreet

modesty

13L. Shyness

skittish

timid

bashful

coy

meek

13M. Dishonesty

dishonest

naughty

sly

tricky

mischievous

underhanded

unfaithful

mischief

cunning

disloyalty

treason

13N. Loyalty/Courage

obedience

allegiance

loyalty

devotion

bravery

grit

chivalry

valor

bold

fearless

adventurous

courageous

gallant

heroic

faithful

loyal

patriotic

straightforward

13O. Instability

frantic

hectic

uncontrolled

unsettled

unsteady

amuck

fanatic

fickle

giddy

unstable

13P. Caution

cautious

stingy

suspicious

wary

---

foolhardy

slack

---

reckless

14. Location/Direction

14A. Location (General)

altitude

position

standpoint

axis

destination

whereabouts

14B. Boundaries

border

boundary

brim

ridge

horizon

rim

verge

brink

flank

battlefront

14C. Planes

horizontal

diagonal

perpendicular

vertical

sideways

broadside

lateral

14D. Non-specific Locations

elsewhere

14E. Directions

midwest

southland

eastward

northeastern

northerly

northernmost

northland

northward

northwestern

southeastern

southward

southwestern

westernmost

westward

starboard

14F. Back-Front-Middle

background

hind

endpoint

fore

obverse

		peak
ahead of	internal	summit
		topside
		pinnacle
halfway	incoming	
medium	intake	upright
mid		
midst		
midway		
	exterior	upland
	outward	skyward
central	overboard	
	external	
		overland
14G. Direction To/From	embark	
bound		
thereto		**14J. Down/Under**
hither		underside
	14I. Up/On	
	thereon	
	hereon	
		underfoot
14H. In/Out and Inward/Outward		
inward	atop	
inland		
interior		downward

66

downwind

thereabouts

14K. Distances

outlying

closeness

contact

vicinity

yonder

homeward

abroad

overseas

14L. Presence/Absence

absence

attendance

presence

beyond

absent

truant

aside

roundabout

local

nigh

abreast

adjacent

thereabout

available

unavailable

15. Literature/Writing

15A. Names/Titles

brand

denomination

trademark

monogram

dub

heading

postmark

subheading

caption

stigma

inscription

15B. Types of Literature

nonfiction

poetry

composition

literature

verse

prose

legend

myth

parable

comedy

fable

15C. Types of Publications

cookbook

schoolbook

textbook

yearbook

catalogue

guidebook

handbook

manual

primer

script

hymnal

biography

diary

essay

novel

autobiography

chapter

paragraph

text

volume

document

edition

episode

issue

pamphlet

paperback

publication

excerpt

manuscript

almanac

atlas

bibliography

thesaurus

scripture

testament

journal

summary

15D. Poems/Songs

lyric

stanza

limerick

refrain

poetic

anthem

ballad

hymn

ditty

psalm

serenade

score

15E. Drawings/Illustrations

diagram

illustration

15F. Messages

telegram

tidings

correspondence

memo

announcement

bulletin

commercial

advertisement

handbill

motto

signpost

slogan

billboard

signboard

15G. Things to Write On/With

stationery

typewriter

pastel

inkstand

inkwell

tablet

parchment

pasteboard

ream

scroll

15H. Rules/Laws

commandment

deed

diploma

curfew

regulation

policy

amendment

charter

constitution

contract

treaty

passport

resolution

warrant

15I. Reading/Writing/Drawing Actions

doodle

shorthand

jot

scrawl

typewrite

publish

draft

illustrate

sketch

watercolor

etch

stencil

indent

punctuate

italicize

misspell		
proofread skim scan browse		
penmanship calligraphy		
handwritten legible		

16. Water/Liquids

16A. Different Forms of Water/Liquids

fluid

moisture

aqua

drizzle

vapor

sleet

snowcap

glacier

hail

hailstone

iceberg

berg

icecap

slush

floe

cascade

surge

ooze

ebb

seep

16B. Actions Related to Water/Liquids

dribble

secrete

squirt

gush

slosh

spatter

spurt

swash

dissolve

evaporate

thaw

ford

wade

snorkel

		evaporation
absorb	## 16C. Equipment Used with Liquids	condensation
penetrate		
drench	waterwheel	
moisten		
submerge		
dilute		
douse		
leach	hydraulic	smog
souse		
waterlog		
	nozzle	
humid	funnel	## 16E. Slime
moist	spout	sediment
slick	valve	silt
soggy		goo
		muck
	## 16D. Moisture	
waterproof	dew	foam
watertight	dewdrop	scum
	droplet	froth

16F. Bodies of Water

tidewater

geyser

outlet

tributary

backwater

eddy

estuary

gusher

headwaters

millpond

runoff

---

swamp

bog

delta

marsh

marshland

lagoon

reef

---

bay

gulf

cove

---

inlet

fjord

---

current

tide

surf

waterline

white cap

---

tidal

16G. Places Near Water

peninsula

isthmus

---

riverside

seacoast

shoreline

waterfront

---

lakeside

mainland

waterside

coastland

headland

sandbank

seaboard

strand

16H. Directions Related to Water

ashore

inland

---

afloat

undersea

downstream

offshore

upstream

midstream

upriver

16I. Man-made Places For/Near Water

port

shipyard

seaport

breakwater

wharf

berth

aquarium

channel

dam

reservoir

aqueduct

canal

dike

moat

sluice

17. Clothing

17A. Clothing (General)

outfit

uniform

attire

wardrobe

apparel

array

garb

garment

lingerie

tuxedo

fashion

fad

style

craze

glamour

17B. Parts of Clothing

lining

seam

ruff

ruffle

tassel

cuff

frill

fringe

pom-pom

17C. Shirts/Pants/Skirts

blouse

jersey

pullover

cardigan

waistband

overalls

slacks

trousers

dungarees

bedclothes

kimono

nightshirt

petticoat

pinafore

17D. Things Worn on the Head

headdress

veil

beret

headpiece

turban

visor

headgear

nightcap

tiara

goggles

spectacles

eyeshade

17E. Things Worn on the Hands/Feet

moccasin

sandal

footwear

snowshoe

garter

mitt

mittens

gauntlet

17F. Coats

poncho

stole

slicker

topcoat

waistcoat

mantle

shawl

cloak

17G. Accessories to Clothing

muffler

sash

kerchief

bandanna

cane

parasol

sunshade

hairpin

razor

jewelry

locket

trinket

bangle

corsage

garland

pendant

scepter

sequin

perfume

cologne

lipstick

cosmetics

rouge

17H. Armor

armor

breastplate

sheath

shield

bulletproof

17I. Actions Related to Clothing

clothe

clad

don

mend

stitch

alter

baste

knit

crochet

embroider

weave

dressmaking

embroidery

wrinkle

crease

furl

pucker

tatter

ravel

rumple

17J. Characteristics of Clothes and Wearing of Clothes

sheer

informal

handmade

fashionable

barefoot

naked

bareheaded

nude

17K. Fabrics

material

cheesecloth

dry goods

fabric

textile

skein

fiber

tint

texture

calfskin

flannel

gauze

nylon

pigskin

sheepskin

buckskin

calico

khaki

linen

plaid

suede

terry

plush

homespun

terry

plush

18. Places Where People Might Live/Dwell

18A. Places Where People Might Live

colony

birthplace

homeland

nationwide

heaven

paradise

wonderland

metropolis

outskirts

suburb

spa

resort

ghetto

slum

province

district

empire

reign

18B. Continents/Countries

continent

continental

Canada

China

France

Germany

Greenland

Holland

Italy

Japan

Mexico

Spain

Iran

Israel

Orient

18C. States

Alabama

18D. Cities

Columbus

Detroit

80

Flagstaff	Montgomery	
Harrisburg	Nashville	
Hartford	Oklahoma City	
Jacksonville	Peoria	
Memphis	Portland	
Milwaukee	Salt Lake City	
New Orleans	Spokane	
Omaha	Springfield	
Philadelphia	Helena	
Phoenix	Reno	
Pittsburgh	Trenton	
Providence		
Richmond		
San Antonio		
Santa Fe		
Seattle		
St. Louis		
Tampa		
Toledo		
Topeka		
Wichita		
Cheyenne		
Cincinnati		
Cleveland		
Des Moines		
Duluth		
Indianapolis		
Kansas City		
Lansing		
Louisville		

19. Noises/Sounds

19A. Noises (General)

echo

peal

trill

audio

blare

eavesdrop

harsh

shrill

deafening

hoarse

hush

lull

breathless

serene

voiceless

soundproof

tranquil

clatter

clamor

commotion

pitch

tone

crescendo

intensity

audible

earshot

hark

19B. Devices That Produce/Reproduce Sound

sonar

earphone

loudspeaker

radiophone

receiver

switchboard

foghorn

gong

siren

chime

firebox

19C. Noises Made by People

applause

fracas

ruckus

rumpus

uproar

ovation

belch

burp

cough

hiccup

snore

burr

wheeze

applaud

chant

holler

bellow

screech

shriek

yodel

snicker

titter

bawl

groan

whine

wail

babble

blurt

mumble

murmur

stammer

stutter

rant

rave

19D. Animal Noises

bleat

chirp

croak

grunt

hiss

hoofbeat

hoot

whinny

yap

cackle

neigh

snarl

yelp

yip

yowl

bray

warble

19E. Noises Made by Objects

clank

click

creak

crunch

gurgle

rattle

rustle

slam

thud

thump

toot

boom

ping

twang

chug		
clang		
clink		
plop		
crackle		
fizz		
plunk		
tinkle		
jangle		

20. Land/Terrain

20A. Areas of Land

acre

acreage

plot

clearing

location

expanse

site

premises

region

territory

zone

frontier

terrain

tropics

domain

outback

20B. Characteristics of Places

geographic

geographical

geological

polar

tropical

coastal

mountainous

rural

rustic

underdeveloped

metropolitan

municipal

urban

wasteland

wilderness

tundra

moor

steppe

20C. Valleys/Craters

cavern

gulley

cove

ravine

dale

glen

gulch

ditch

pit

cavity

shaft

trench

furrow

silo

gap

notch

cranny

groove

cleft

crevice

rift

rut

crater

chasm

20D. Mountains/Hills

alp

butte

dune

mesa

sierra

volcano

foothill

tableland

highland

knoll

watershed

hilltop

mountainside

ridge

bluff

crag

crest

embankment

slope

20E. Forests/Woodlands

grove

thicket

woodland

backwoods

timberland

glade

20F. Fields/Pastures

farmland

hayfield

prairie

countryside

paddy

vineyard

grassland

lowland

battlefield

battleground

20G. Yards/Parks

churchyard

courtyard

brickyard

graveyard

patio

plaza

dooryard

20H. Bodies in Space

global

universe

galaxy

cosmos

constellation

lunar

solar

celestial

stellar

Jupiter

Mars

Mercury

Neptune

Pluto

Saturn

Uranus

Venus

comet

meteor

satellite

eclipse

21. Dwellings/Shelters

21A. Man-made Structures

icehouse

structure

silo

construction

establishment

installation

21B. Places to Live

cottage

countryhouse

chalet

dwelling

habitat

homestead

suite

summerhouse

barracks

bungalow

dormitory

hovel

shanty

villa

manor

mansion

estate

igloo

teepee

wigwam

hogan

lodge

bunkhouse

21C. Places of Protection/Incarceration

fort

blockhouse

dugout

fortress

garrison

outpost

pueblo

acropolis

bunker

fortification

stronghold

haven

refuge

windbreak

retreat

dungeon

prison

quarantine

stockade

poorhouse

guardhouse

guardroom

21D. Places Where Goods Are Bought and Sold

booth

salon

barbershop

bookstore

pharmacy

cafe

cafeteria

saloon

smokehouse

coffeehouse

21E. Mills/Factories/Offices

headquarters

studio

workhouse

workshop

sawmill

lumberyard

tannery

refinery

21F. Places for Learning/Experimentation

college

campus

university

academy

seminary

gallery

lab

laboratory

planetarium

observatory

reactor

21G. Places for Sports/Entertainment

auditorium

arena

coliseum

grandstand

opera

stadium

theater

ringside

gym

21H. Medical Facilities

clinic

ward

morgue

mortuary

21I. Places for Worship/Meetings

chapel

mission

temple

monastery

cathedral

convent

shrine

synagogue

capitol

courthouse

courtroom

21J. Places Related to Transportation

depot

terminal

21K. Places Used for Storage

boathouse

hayloft

shack

storehouse

woodshed

warehouse

arsenal

greenhouse

hothouse

21L. Farms/Ranches

plantation

fishery

21M. Monuments

memorial

landmark

monument

sphinx

totem

gravestone		
headstone		
tomb		
tombstone		

22. Materials and Building

22A. Containers

carton

packet

capsule

cartridge

compartment

cubbyhole

socket

coffin

crate

pillbox

tinderbox

dropper

test tube

envelope

parcel

cargo

freight

shipload

shipment

wagonload

carload

cartload

barrel

cask

hogshead

hopper

keg

bin

sandbag

breadbasket

hamper

flask

jug

waterbottle

canteen

coffeepot

wide-mouthed

scuttle

basin

tank

washbasin

washbowl

cistern

trough

vat

washtub

---

luggage

suitcase

baggage

knapsack

packsack

valise

22B. Materials/Objects Used to Cover Things

cork

stopper

thimble

wrapper

bung

---

canvas

tarpaulin

---

cellophane

22C. Wooden Building Materials

lumber

basswood

hardwood

plywood

sandalwood

timber

veneer

---

driftwood

pillar

palette

panel

plank

shingle

slat

wallboard

22D. Other Building Materials

cement

pavement

plaster

adobe

asbestos

brickwork

ceramic

concrete

grout

porcelain

putty

tar

tile

brownstone

clapboard

mortar

stucco

---

cornerstone

---

drainpipe

sewer

culvert

duct

pipeline

waterspout

---

crossbar

rung

stilt

---

support

prop

pedestal

---

brace

bracket

crosspiece

22E. General Names for Objects

material

22F. Building/Repairing Actions

construction

earthwork

formation

groundwork

---

construct

create

establish

manufacture

generate

---

develop

pave

forge

install

process

glaze

---

adjust

modernize

modify

preserve

qualify

rearrange

rebuild

restore

strengthen

rehabilitate

streamline

---

maintenance

22G. Wrapping/Packing Actions

bind

furl

unravel

23. The Human Body

23A. The Body (General)

mental

physical

---

breast

thorax

bosom

limbs

rump

teat

udder

nape

scruff

---

spinal

---

waistline

23B. Body Coverings

flesh

scalp

blubber

dandruff

pore

tissue

membrane

---

suntan

complexion

---

ruddy

---

mustache

pigtail

redhead

sideburns

tuft

---

cowlick

hairline

tress

---

bearded

redhaired

---

bruise

freckle

birthmark

hump

pimple

rash

tumor

wart

blackhead

blemish

pock

23C. The Head

skull

ego

forehead
countenance

23D. Mouth/Throat

jaw
fang
cuspid
molar

dental
oral

windpipe

23E. Eyes/Ears/Nose

earlobe
lobe

brow
eyeball
eyebrow
eyelash
eyelid
retina

eyesight

nostril

23F. Limbs

shoulders
armpit
biceps

knuckle
thumbnail
cuticle

23G. Legs/Feet

ankle
arch
flatfoot

calves
crotch
shank
shin
thigh

23H. Organs of the Body

gut

intestine

kidney

liver

diaphragm

gland

lung

ovary

bowel

spleen

23I. Body Fluids

blood

perspiration

sweat

bloodstream

mucus

saliva

hemoglobin

capillary

vein

vessel

artery

ventricle

circulate

clot

23J. Bones/Muscles/Nerves

backbone

breastbone

cheekbone

collarbone

spine

jawbone

vertebrae

muscle

cartilage

ligament

sinew

tendon

nerve

23K. Body Systems

circulatory

digestive

reproductive

respiratory

sensory

skeletal

circulation

digestion

digest		
perspire		

24. Vegetation

24A. Vegetation (General)

oasis

shrub

arbor

vegetation

flora

greenery

underbrush

undergrowth

24B. Types of Trees/Bushes

aspen

birch

cedar

cottonwood

maple

redwood

balsa

beech

boxwood

citrus

dogwood

hickory

laurel

locust

spruce

eucalyptus

evergreen

hemlock

teak

24C. Parts of Trees/Bushes

bough

knothole

stump

thorn

wicker

broadleaf

offshoot

sprig

foliage

latex

pith

resin

24D. Flowers/Plants

bouquet

pod

cottonseed

spore

sprout

tuber

linseed

buttercup

carnation

geranium

goldenrod

lily

marigold

petunia

rosebud

snapdragon

sunflower

wildflower

bluebell

chrysanthemum

cowslip

flytrap

foxglove

gardenia

honeysuckle

larkspur

anemone

holly

huckleberry

thistle

brier

flax

hemp

jute

24E. Other Vegetation

algae

fungus

toadstool

kelp

mildew

thatch

lichen

beanstalk

grapevine

stalk

vine

cornhusk

husk

rind

alfalfa

bamboo

cornstalk

reed

haystack

sagebrush

seaweed

milkweed

ragweed

25. Groups of Things

25A. General Names for Groups of Things

assortment

collection

array

collective

---

arrangement

directory

file

menu

series

setup

curriculum

inventory

invoice

roster

timetable

chronology

classification

sequence

---

combination

compound

mixture

alloy

composite

medley

hybrid

---

web

network

---

bale

batch

clump

cluster

stock

sheaf

wad

swath

---

collect

organize

summarize

assemble

classify

muster

cumulate

25B. Groups of People/Animals

gang

huddle

faction

horde

mass

mob

throng

---

chorus

quartet

trio

ensemble

quintet

cowherd

flock

brood

covey

pod

bevy

gaggle

---

brotherhood

fraternity

denomination

---

species

phylum

---

crew

posse

25C. Political/Social Groups

confederacy

democracy

federation

---

republic

protectorate

---

national

international

---

congress

legislature

parliament

senate

regime

---

lawmaking

federal

legislative

political

---

civilization

culture

society

---

clan

caste

cult

sect

---

tribal

civic

25D. Groups in Uniform

air force

navy

infantry

marines

---

patrol

troop

squad

squadron

brigade

corp

detail

legion

regiment

congregation

25E. Social/Business Groups

committee

council

organization

staff

union

association

auxiliary

foundation

league

troupe

commission

institute

membership

partnership

conference

convention

session

assembly

audience

roundup

26. Value/Correctness

26A. Right/Wrong

truth

justice

reality

---

crime

error

failure

blunder

flaw

lapse

wrongdoing

shortcoming

---

actual

accurate

constitutional

genuine

lawful

legal

authentic

moral

rightful

---

valid

---

acceptable

appropriate

apt

precise

satisfactory

suitable

eligible

realistic

---

incorrect

lawless

---

faulty

unfit

---

honesty

fairness

---

innocence

---

honest

innocent

decent

honorable

forthcoming

wholesome

26B. Success/Failure

deserve

qualify

succeed

merit

---

muff

fail

err

bungle

bumble

26C. Importance/Value

basic

lifesaving

necessary

primary

urgent

essential

vital

acute

critical

crucial

fundamental

organic

underlying

---

base

essence

---

super

superior

absolute

prime

superb

supreme

sublime

---

beloved

precious

delightful

desirable

memorable

impressive

---

valuable

noteworthy

worthwhile

---

dandy

excellent

glorious

magnificent

remarkable

fabulous

fantastic

incredible

marvelous

outstanding

regal

splendid

terrific

tremendous

exceptional

extraordinary

invaluable

presidential

spectacular

---

miraculous

---

practical

adequate

usable

---

value

usefulness

26D. Lack of Value

useless

unimportant

worthless

insignificant petty	ridiculous absurd	
inferior shabby shoddy		
dreadful horrible negative corrupt		
dire sinister unfavorable		
foul grim ghastly ghostly		

27. Similarity/Dissimilarity

27A. Likeness

likeness

equality

similarity

comparison

metaphor

analogy

agreement

accord

harmony

congruent

equal

related

similar

consistent

equivalent

compatible

ditto

identical

approximate

parallel

resemble

conform

example

imitation

replacement

substitute

artificial

synthetic

echo

imitate

counterfeit

mimic

duplicate

mimeograph

27B. Addition (Relationship Markers)

as well as

as well

equally

for example

further

in addition

moreover

furthermore

likewise

actually

namely

27C. Difference

variety

variation

contrary

separate

unlike

various

lopsided

unequal

freak

quirk

temper

adapt

develop

differ

molt

undergo

vary

reform

transform

development

metamorphosis

27D. Contrast (Relationship Markers)

compare

contrast

otherwise

alternately

alternatively

by comparison

comparative

in comparison

on the contrary

on the other hand

or rather

versus

whereas

either...or

neither...nor

except

except for

however

anyhow

at any rate

in any case

in any event

nevertheless

regardless of

despite

nonetheless

notwithstanding

109

28. Money/Finance

28A. Money/Goods You Receive

savings

fortune
windfall

allowance
salary
income
wage

contribution
grant
scholarship

legacy

credit
gain
profit

bounty
premium

insurance

28B. Money/Goods Paid Out

fee
tab
bail
fare
mortgage
tariff
tax
toll
levy

taxation

dues
expense
payment
price

loss
debt

handout

28C. Types of Money/Goods

cash
wealth
capital
fund
payroll

finance	redeem	**28E. Money Related to Characteristics**
		costly
		expensive
		royal
		wasteful
		posh
shilling	owe	
guinea	purchase	
	render	
	subscribe	
	donate	
	splurge	
		luxury
coupon		
postage		
receipt		
token		
	repay	cheap
		inexpensive
souvenir		
stock		
ware	lease	
merchandise	discount	humble
	auction	needy
	peddle	
	ransom	
	retail	
28D. Money/Goods Related to Actions		poverty
afford		
budget		
scrimp	bargain	
invest		**28F. Places Where Money/Goods Are Kept**
insure		account

111

vault

mint

strongbox

pocketbook

billfold

checkbook

wallet

bankbook

moneybag

marketplace

commerce

economy

29. Soil/Metal/Rock

29A. Metals

aluminum

mercury

zinc

tungsten

---

brass

bronze

steel

tole

alloy

chrome

ore

solder

---

carbon

calcium

manganese

radium

silicon

uranium

barium

beryllium

cobalt

---

phosphorus

potassium

sulphur

---

flint

quartz

bauxite

feldspar

gneiss

graphite

lodestone

mica

talc

---

lava

magma

obsidian

pumice

soapstone

29B. Jewels/Rocks

crystal

jewel

pearl

ruby

emerald

gem

opal

turquoise

amethyst

jade

topaz

---

boulder

limestone

marble

sandstone

shale

bedrock

cobblestone

granite

gravel

nugget

rubble

slate

aggregate

asphalt

charcoal

coal

coke

anthracite

grindstone

millstone

29C. Characteristics of Rocks/Soil

pebble

volcanic

sedimentary

barren

fallow

29D. Actions of Metals

rust

corrode

oxidize

tarnish

29E. Soil

humus

loam

peat

sod

topsoil

turf

clod

dung

manure

dunghill

29F. Actions Done to Soil/Crops

harrow

irrigate

tend

cultivate

fertilize

grub

thresh

irrigation

cultivation

30. Rooms/Furnishing/Parts of Dwellings/Buildings

30A. Rooms

ballroom

cloakroom

closet

den

nursery

pantry

playroom

veranda

washroom

chamber

loft

parlor

showroom

stateroom

wardroom

aisle

archway

hallway

lobby

corridor

portal

threshold

30B. Parts of a Home

fireplace

fireside

smokestack

flue

hearth

mantel

mantelpiece

stovepipe

hearthstone

baseboard

dome

housetop

steeple

eaves

spire

shopwindow

shutter

windowseat

windowsill

awning

lattice

vent

dormer

latticework

wicket

stairway

bannister

staircase

stile

doorpost

doorplate

doorstone

jamb

30C. Fences/Ledges

ledge

curb

gutter

barbed wire

gatepost

gateway

hedge

trellis

30D. Furniture

furniture

decor

furnishing

counter

worktable

altar

drainboard

pulpit

tabletop

bleacher

rocker

sofa

wheelchair

workbench

armchair

couch

pew

throne

bookcase

cupboard

hutch

nook

cabinet

washstand

bureau

sideboard

cot

cradle

crib

fourposters

mattress

headboard

30E. Decorations

decoration

ornament

accessory

knickknack

trifle

decorate

beautify

furnish

varnish

upholster

adorn

wallpaper

canopy

linoleum

tapestry

banner

pennant

spangle

tinsel

wreath

116

confetti

plaque

ironwork

centerpiece

flowerpot

pottery

vase

cornucopia

earthenware

cut glass

urn

homemade

domestic

30F. Linens

bedspread

drape

quilt

bedroll

napkin

tablecloth

doily

dishcloth

pad

cushion

hassock

31. Attitudinals

31A. Attitudinals (Truth)

actually

definitely

frankly

honestly

basically

doubtless

essentially

obviously

truthfully

undoubtedly

candidly

fundamentally

literally

undeniably

unquestionably

ideally

apparently

evidently

technically

strictly

seriously

bluntly

31B. Attitudinals (Lack of Truth/Doubt)

possibly

conceivably

presumably

reportedly

seemingly

superficially

supposedly

theoretically

31C. Attitudinals (Expected/Unexpected)

unexpectedly

oddly

ironically

appropriately

typically

inevitably

naturally

predictably

understandably

remarkably

amazingly

astonishingly

incredibly

refreshingly

31D. Attitudinals (Fortunate/Unfortunate)

fortunately

delightfully

unfortunately

unluckily

tragically

31E. Attitudinals (Satisfaction/Dissatisfaction)

disappointingly

annoyingly

disturbingly

regrettably

31F. Attitudinals (Correctness/Incorrectness)

justly

incorrectly

unjustly

31G. Attitudinals (Wisdom/Lack of Wisdom)

reasonably

shrewdly

artfully

sensibly

unwisely

31H. Other Attitudinals

preferably

32. Shapes/Dimensions

32A. Shapes (General Names)

outline

profile

contour

silhouette

skyline

framework

32B. Circular or Curved Shapes

cylinder

halo

sphere

crescent

disk

coil

spiral

arc

circuit

flex

warp

curvature

kink

parabola

circular

concave

convex

spherical

32C. Rectangular or Square Shapes

parallelogram

polygon

hexagon

octagon

pentagon

trapezoid

equilateral

quadrilateral

rectangular

triangular

isometric

prism

pyramid

cubic

32D. Straightness/Crookedness

zigzag

crisscross

fillet

beeline

linear

sinuous

32E. Sharpness/Bluntness

blunt

keen

flatten

sharpen

32F. Dimension

broad

threadlike

width

dense

depth

density

shallow

trim

tier

extend

thicken

widen

deepen

lengthen

32G. Fullness/Emptiness

swollen

fraught

null

void

exhaust

deflate

deplete

32H. Inclination

plumb

slant

steep

tilt

incline

erect

32H. Inclination

plumb

33. Destructive and Helpful Actions

33A. Actions Destructive to Nonhumans

breakdown

collision

mishap

chip

mar

nick

crush

damage

mash

puncture

shatter

squelch

erode

fracture

mangle

rupture

destroy

demolish

extinguish

devastate

snuff

wreckage

destruction

33B. Actions Destructive to Humans

abuse

injure

molest

offend

rape

ambush

murder

slaughter

slay

execute

massacre

persecute

suicide

overwhelm

paralyze

stun

afflict

beset

cripple

deadly

painful

fatal

poisonous

penal

discipline

horsewhip

scourge

vengeance

prosecute

torment

torture

33C. Fighting

duel

struggle

wrestle

challenge

clash

raid

repel

rumble

scuffle

skirmish

invade

battle

friction

revolution

bloodshed

combat

conflict

fray

showdown

strife

warpath

disturbance

riot

unrest

warfare

invasion

onslaught

siege

peace

33D. Actions Helpful to Humans

assist

accommodate

avail

contribute

relieve

foster

nourish

promote

enable

improve

enrich

guide

escort

protector

aid

cure

heal

recover

refresh

defend		
rescue		
fend		
safeguard		
sake		
stead		
behalf		
benefit		

34. Sports/Recreation

34A. Sports/Recreation

hobby

sport

recreation

championship

competition

derby

marathon

tournament

compete

34B. Specific Sports

hockey

soccer

softball

volleyball

lacrosse

polo

golf

tennis

badminton

croquet

backhand

skiing

steeplechase

wrestling

34C. Equipment Used in Sports/Recreation

base

bat

beanbag

Maypole

putter

racket

ski

tee

backstop

dumbbell

surfboard

target

hurdle

puck

hammock

trapeze

carousel

goal

inning

knockout

tackle

volley

bunt homer	horseplay	poker whist
backfield defense offense	**34E. Magic** stunt witchcraft gimmick sorcery astrology	checkerboard dice chessboard sandbox ace
34D. Exercising exercise workout jogging sprinting yoga	magical	
stretch jog sprint	**34F. Board and Other Games** checkers crossword tiddlywinks chess raffle	
cartwheel somersault	checkmate	

35. Language

35A. Language and Language Conventions

grammar

slang

vocabulary

dialect

idiom

accent

pronunciation

emphasis

lisp

diction

capitalization

hyphen

parenthesis

colon

35B. Words/Sentences

phrase

clause

password

abbreviation

prefix

suffix

syllable

affix

exclamatory

interrogative

superlative

adjective

antonym

conjunction

predicate

preposition

synonym

modifier

participle

homonym

pun

homograph

homophone

35C. Letters/Alphabet

beta

cuneiform

alpha

italics

alphabetically

phonetic		
cipher notation		

36. Ownership/Possession

36A. Losing/Giving Up

abandon

misplace

displace

dismiss

dispose

discard

eject

barter

exchange

lease

loan

lend

swap

36B. Freedom/Lack of Freedom

getaway

parole

release

cede

turnover

sacrifice

surrender

36C. Possession/Ownership

possession

property

custody

ownership

monopoly

maintain

occupy

possess

36D. Winning/Losing

conquer

defeat

subdue

excel

overcome

overrun

overtake

overthrow

prevail

success

accomplishment

triumph

conquest

dominant

triumphant

loss

downfall

failure

washout

champion

victor

36E. Taking/Receiving Actions

regain

attain

obtain

reap

achieve

acquire

extract

accept

attract

receive

trespass

inherit

arrest

capture

kidnap

abduct

holdup

loot

plunder

hijack

ransack

36F. Finding/Keeping

locate

distinguish

pinpoint

tuck

conserve

reserve

withhold

hoard

restrict

retain

disguise

conceal

camouflage

131

37. Disease/Health

37A. Disease

disease

sickness

symptom

illness

infection

injury

sane

wholesome

condition

health

sanity

blindness

starvation

blind

deaf

lame

mute

contagious

seasick

stricken

37B. Specific Diseases/Ailments

cancer

croup

polio

rabies

scurvy

beriberi

diphtheria

influenza

malaria

smallpox

tuberculosis

37C. Symptoms of Diseases

itch

earache

fever

headache

toothache

coma

exhaustion

nausea

pang

twinge

vomit

weariness

epidemic

plague

famine

healthful

hale

robust

fatigue	**37E. Actions Related to Injury/Disease**	transfusion
impair	blister	
	frostbite	operate
dizzy	scab	diagnose
numb	whiplash	transplant
raw	abscess	dissect
sore	concussion	inoculate
exhausted	fester	
groggy	gash	aspirin
delirious	venom	iodine
feverish	welt	pill
		antibiotics
		antidote
	poison	ointment
	sprain	penicillin
37D. Specific Types of Germs/Genes	cripple	potion
bacteria	infect	prescription
virus	paralyze	vaccine
microbe		vitamin
organism		dose
	37F. Medicine	narcotic
	operation	serum
septic	surgery	tonic
	treatment	
	vaccination	
	remedy	
	therapy	

bandage		
cast		
sling		
crutch		
splint		

38. Light

38A. Light/Lightness

daylight

candlelight

firelight

starlight

gleam

gloss

glimmer

glint

luster

sheen

brightness

lightness

wavelength

brilliant

radiant

vivid

luminous

38B. Actions of Light

glisten

glitter

glow

twinkle

dazzle

radiate

shimmer

brighten

lighten

reflect

illuminate

38C. Darkness

gloom

haze

shady

somber

darken

fade

blur

blacken

splotch

38D. Producers of Light

flare

torch

beacon

torchlight

candlestick

lantern

lamppost

searchlight

skylight

bulb

lightbulb

filament

moonbeam

ray

sunbeam

laser

sunspot

38E. Clarity

clarity

transparent

drab

fuzzy

murky

indefinite

opaque

vague

39. Causality

39A. Causality

effect

result

conclusion

outcome

aftereffect

consequence

impact

---

purpose

intent

stimulus

agent

incentive

motive

---

stimulate

initiate

spearhead

---

vary

affect

impress

influence

induce

39B. Causality (Relationship Markers)

because of

in that

so that

hereby

hereupon

herewith

whereas

whereby

---

for as much

for the fact that

herein

on account of

therefrom

wherefore

---

therefore

thus

accordingly

as a consequence

as a result

for all that

lest

thereby

consequently

hence

whereupon

in that case

wherewith

if only

if...then

now that

138

40. Weather

40A. Weather/Nature (General)

climate

nature

environment

atmosphere

atmospheric

40B. Storms/Wind

blizzard

hailstorm

downpour

rainstorm

thundershower

cloudburst

monsoon

torrent

sandstorm

twister

whirlwind

windstorm

cyclone

gale

gust

hurricane

squall

tempest

tornado

chinook

typhoon

thunderstorm

thunderbolt

thunderclap

40C. Clouds

cirrus

cumulus

thundercloud

cirrocumulus

cirrostratus

cumulonimbus

thunderhead

40D. Natural Catastrophes

drought

earthquake

flood

avalanche

landslide

blight

disaster

emergency

catastrophe

tragedy

calamity

crisis

ordeal

disastrous

40E. Characteristics of Weather

icy

muggy

overcast

wintry

arid

sultry

41. Cleanliness/Uncleanliness

41A. Filth/Uncleanliness

junk

junkyard

litter

pollution

slop

wastepaper

clutter

filth

grime

rubbish

sewage

debris

eyesore

impurity

pollute

infect

contaminate

smear

smudge

streak

bloodstain

darken

blacken

daub

defile

foul

nasty

bleak

dismal

dreary

filthy

dingy

41B. Cleanliness

bathe

clean-up

polish

rinse

shoeshine

wax

whitewash

buff

launder

manicure

turnout

preen

scour

swab

sanitary

sterile

hygiene

immaculate

cleanliness

sanitation

draft

filter

pasteurize

purify

strain

purge

sterilize

41C. Tools for Cleaning		
broomstick		
washboard		
vacuum		
detergent		
lotion		
shampoo		
lather		
lye		
soapsuds		
suds		
bleach		
toothbrush		
toothpaste		
toothpick		
floss		

142

42. Popularity/Familiarity

42A. Popularity/Familiarity

popular

public

legendary

prominent

---

ordinary

regular

commonplace

normal

traditional

typical

widespread

accustomed

customary

mainstream

norm

par

pedestrian

standard

universal

---

patent

obvious

conspicuous

evident

---

fame

appeal

attraction

dignity

glory

recognition

limelight

repute

42B. Lack of Popularity/Familiarity

privacy

secrecy

solitude

---

private

unfamiliar

unknown

anonymous

undiscovered

42C. Likelihood

definite

absolute

---

probable

contingent

liable

---

doubtful

mysterious

uncertain

ambiguous

---

accidental

doom

hazard

casual

jinx

random		
bid stake gamble venture		
fate fluke miracle boon		

43. Physical Traits of People

43A. Physical Traits

athletic

muscular

rugged

---

powerful

potent

powerhouse

---

health

strength

vigor

agility

brawn

gusto

---

awkward

clumsy

gawky

---

agile

graceful

spry

---

frail

puny

rawboned

rickety

scrawny

feeble

gaunt

---

handicap

weakness

43B. Neatness

messy

sloppy

---

tangle

windblown

---

tidy

prim

shipshape

43C. Attractiveness

sightly

attractive

bonny

comely

exquisite

---

elegant

adorable

formal

classic

gorgeous

majestic

sleek

homely

unattractive

hideous

43D. Size as a Physical Trait

skinny

slender

slight

slim

lanky

scrag

dainty

chubby

plump

flabby

pudgy

burly

stout

potbelly

44. Touching/Grabbing Actions

44A. Feeling/Striking Actions

stroke

grope

caress

fondle

knead

massage

dab

nudge

spur

butt

jab

rap

prod

lash

punch

smack

whack

wham

buffet

lob

thrash

whop

putt

wallop

44B. Grabbing/Holding Actions

clasp

clutch

grip

nab

clench

grasp

secure

wring

clinch

vise

pinch

strum

tweeze

nip

pluck

cling

cuddle

nuzzle

embrace

snuggle

44C. Specific Actions Done with the Hands		
fumble		
shrug		
handshake		
salute		
wield		

45. Pronouns

45A. Pronouns and Reflexive Pronouns

thee

thou

thy

thyself

oneself

45B. Possessive Pronouns

theirs

45C. Relative Pronouns

whom

45D. Interrogative Pronouns

whatever

whichever

whomever

45E. Indefinite Pronouns

whoever

whomsoever

45F. Interrogative/Indefinite Adverbs

whenever

wherever

someway

whensoever

46. Contractions

46A. Contractions (Not)

aren't

doesn't

hadn't

hasn't

wasn't

wouldn't

ain't

mustn't

46B. Contractions (Have)

we've

46C. Contractions (Will)

there'll

46D. Contractions (Is)

'tis

here's

what's

where's

47. Entertainment/The Arts

47A. Plays/Movies

performance

program

scene

matinee

rehearsal

tryout

perform

audition

drama

film

movie

comedy

preview

skit

cinema

newsreel

radiobroadcast

vaudeville

plot

setting

climax

scenery

stage

background

backstage

offstage

47B. Music/Dance

chord

melody

treble

octave

jazz

stave

unison

musical

concert

orchestra

opera

symphony

jig

polka

waltz

minuet

solo

duet

conduct

47C. Instruments

accordion

cymbal

keyboard

organ

percussion

tamborine

tom-tom

xylophone

castanets

glockenspiel

kettledrum

spinet

drumstick

clarinet

flute

oboe

piccolo

saxophone

trombone

tuba

alto

bagpipe

bugle

cornet

recorder

trumpet

mouthpiece

woodwind

banjo

cello

fiddle

viola

lute

lyre

mandolin

tuning fork

47D. Art

photography

woodcraft

photo

mural

photograph

portrait

snapshot

mosaic

sculpture

48. Walking/Running Actions

48A. Running/Walking Actions

lope

scamper

jog

romp

footwork

frisk

prance

ramble

hike

stride

stroll

amble

pace

plod

promenade

strut

swagger

trudge

gait

toddle

tread

limp

shuffle

stumble

waddle

hobble

shamble

stagger

48B. Lurking/Creeping

slink

prowl

sneak

lurk

slither

48C. Kicking

tramp

stomp

trample

48D. Jumping

leap

lurch

coil

lunge

pounce

bound

48E. Standing/Stationary Actions

pose

straddle

bowlegged		
prone		
posture		

49. Mathematics

49A. Branches of Mathematics

math

mathematics

algebra

geometry

trigonometry

49B. Mathematical Quantities

maximum

minimum

average

fraction

sum

total

gross

percent

median

multiple

percentage

proportion

ratio

sine

49C. Mathematical Terms

equation

formula

quotient

exponent

49D. Mathematical Operation

division

multiplication

divisible

divide

multiply

tally

per

50. Auxiliary/Helping Verbs

50A. Auxiliary Verbs

being

50B. Primary Auxiliaries

have

50C. Modals

used to

50D. Semi-Auxiliaries

had best

is bound to

50E. Linking Verbs

becoming

51. Events

51A. Dates/Events (General)

affair

event

experience

happening

development

incident

occasion

instance

occurrence

attempt

deed

project

enterprise

feat

condition

situation

environment

circumstance

context

51B. Festive/Recreational Events

holiday

honeymoon

pastime

leisure

anniversary

celebration

festival

ceremony

bazaar

debut

graduation

caravan

procession

carnival

bullfight

amusement

entertainment

51C. Political Events

election

campaign

vote		
elect		
nominate		
voter		
ballot		

52. Temperature/Fire

52A. Temperature

centigrade

Fahrenheit

thermal

arctic

frigid

chill

temperate

lukewarm

warmth

52B. Insulation

insulation

insulator

insulate

fireproof

52C. Fire

blaze

backfire

combustion

inferno

wildfire

torch

ignite

scorch

singe

kindle

sizzle

arson

flicker

stoke

smolder

52D. Products of Fire

ash

cinder

ember

smut

smokey

52E. Fire Products

matchbox

paraffin

wick

tinder

woodpile

extinguisher

cigar

tobacco

cigarette

53. Images/Perceptions

53A. Visual Images/Perception

appearance

image

reflection

portrayal

representation

scene

view

demonstration

panorama

vision

prospect

farsighted

visual

blindfold

distract

witness

observer

onlooker

represent

reveal

display

reflect

portray

flaunt

emblem

53B. Looking/Perceiving Actions

behold

monitor

scout

snoop

verify

loom

reappear

glance

glimpse

squint

glare

peer

gape

glower

attend

observe

recognize

detect

distinguish

identify

perceive		
snub ignore shun		
focus		
vigil		

54. Life/Survival

54A. Life, Birth, Death

death

sex

childbirth

existence

pollination

reproduction

afterlife

entity

exist

subsist

mortal

animate

earthborn

inhabit

dwell

reside

perish

suffocate

mummy

nonliving

deathbed

extinct

carcass

corpse

burial

funeral

inter

pollinate

breed

reproduce

conceive

incubate

populate

spawn

childbearing

fertile

pregnant

childbed

gene

genetic

natal

54B. Survival/Growth

stamina

endurance

survival

tolerance

survive

163

withstand		
endure		
tolerate		
thrive		
flourish		
prosper		
mature		
evolve		

55. Conformity/Complexity

55A. Conformity to a Norm

original

distinct

scarce

distinctive

rare

uncommon

unique

foreign

peculiar

quaint

weird

bizarre

eccentric

grotesque

outlandish

uncanny

unfinished

incomplete

55B. Complexity/Order

complex

ornate

elaborate

intricate

technical

wrought

maze

confusion

disorder

rout

tangle

bedlam

disarray

muddle

turmoil

balance

symmetry

cosmos

equilibrium

blank

bleak

void

balanced		
steady		
unbroken		
uniform		
neutral		
offset		
unchanged		

56. Difficulty/Danger

56A. Difficulty/Ease	56B. Danger/Safety	treacherous
convenient	prevention	
fluent		
		harmless
	protective	secure
simplify	defensive	immune
ease	hazard	
cinch	risk	
convenience	jeopardy	
	peril	
	pitfall	
backbreaking		
tiresome		
troublesome		
uneasy	endanger	
unbearable		
grueling		
	harmful	
predicament	unsafe	
	hazardous	
	breakneck	
	perilous	

57. Texture/Durability

57A. Texture

texture

tangible

rigid
solid
tough
taut

coarse
rough
porous
prickly
stony

choppy

shaggy
spongy

57B. Durability

durability

sturdy
airtight
durable
potent

brittle
flimsy
ramshackle
makeshift
perishable

deciduous
delicate

frail
finespun
fragile
subtle

57C. Consistency

soften
harden
stiffen
gel

58. Color

58A. Color

beige

hazel

lavender

taupe

violet

amber

azure

buff

magenta

maroon

roan

scarlet

tawny

vermilion

crimson

ecru

indigo

livid

mauve

nutbrown

russet

tangerine

colorless

chromatic

iridescent

golden haired

grey-headed

greyhaired

blonde

brunette

towhead

hue

pigment

dapple

tinge

58B. Paint

tint

whitewash

dye

enamel

lacquer

59. Chemicals

59A. Chemicals

chemical

compound

litmus

---

hydrogen

nitrogen

boron

---

chlorinate

ferment

carbonate

---

chlorine

neon

sodium

bromine

krypton

---

chlorophyll

enzyme

---

dioxide

ammonia

nitrate

oxide

phosphate

sulfate

59B. Acids

acid

caustic

---

hydrochloric

sulfuric

60. Facial Expressions/Actions

60A. Facial Expressions

blush

scowl

smirk

sneer

simper

60B. Actions Associated with the Nose

snore

inhale

perfume

scent

stink

aroma

fragrance

fragrant

fume

incense

reek

odor

stench

60C. Actions Associated with the Mouth

suck

slobber

spew

spit

60D. Breathing

exhale

whiff

respire

choke

strangle

61. Electricity/Particles of Matter

61A. Electricity

electrical

electronic

hydroelectric

electromagnetic

radiation

radioactive

61B. Molecules/Atoms

molecule

molecular

atom

electron

neutron

nucleus

proton

ion

nuclei

isotope

atomic

Clusters in Alphabetical Order

174

Index

aspen, 24B
asphalt, 29B
aspirin, 37F
assemble, 25A
assembly, 25E
assign, 12J
assist, 33D
assistant, 1B
associate, 2V
association, 25E
assortment, 25A
assume, 12D
assure, 10D
astonish, 5J
astonishingly, 31C
astonishment, 5J
astrology, 34E
astronaut, 1L
astronomer, 1L
astronomy, 1L
at any rate, 27D
at first, 7G
at least, 3J
at the same time, 7I
at this point, 7I
athlete, 1D
athletic, 43A
atlas, 15C
atmosphere, 40A
atmospheric, 40A
atom, 61B
atomic, 61B
atop, 14I
attach, 2V
attacker, 9G
attain, 36E
attempt, 51A
attend, 53B
attendance, 14L
attendant, 1B
attentive, 13A
attire, 17A
attorney, 1Y
attract, 36E
attraction, 42A
attractive, 43C

attribute, 5R
auction, 28D
audible, 19A
audience, 25E
audio, 19A
audition, 47A
auditorium, 21G
authentic, 26A
authority, 10G
auto, 11A
autobiography, 15C
automatic, 7J
automatically, 7J
auxiliary, 25E
avail, 33D
available, 14L
avalanche, 40D
average, 49B
aviation, 11G
avoid, 2F
aw, 10K
await, 2B
awe, 5J, 10D
awkward, 43A
awning, 30B
ax, 8F
axe, 8F
axis, 14A
axle, 11F
ay, 10K
aye, 10K
azure, 58A

B

babble, 19C
bachelor, 9C
backbone, 23J
backbreaking, 56A
backfield, 34C
backfire, 52C
background, 14F, 47A
backhand, 34B
backstage, 47A
backstop, 34C
backwater, 16F
backwoods, 20E
bacteria, 37D
bad tempered, 5G
badger, 4E
badminton, 34B
baggage, 22A
bagpipe, 47C
bail, 28B
bait, 10E
balance, 55B
balanced, 55B
bale, 25A
balk, 5I
ballad, 15D
ballot, 51C
ballplayer, 1D
ballroom, 30A
balsa, 24B
bamboo, 24E
ban, 10G
bandage, 37F
bandanna, 17G
bangle, 17G

banjo, 47C
bankbook, 28F
banner, 30E
bannister, 30B
banquet, 6A
barb, 8F
barbed wire, 30C
barber, 1N
barbershop, 21D
bareback, 4O
barefoot, 17J
bareheaded, 17J
barely, 3J
bargain, 28D
barge, 11E
barium, 29A
barley, 6J
baron, 1C
barracks, 21B
barrel, 22A
barren, 29C
barrow, 11B
bartender, 1a
barter, 36A
base, 26C, 34C
baseboard, 30B
baseman, 1D
bashful, 13L
basic, 26C
basically, 31A
basin, 22A
bass, 4H
basswood, 22C
baste, 17I
bat, 34C
batch, 25A
bathe, 41B
baton, 8J
batter, 1D
battle, 33C
battlefield, 20F
battlefront, 14B
battleground, 20F
battleship, 11E
bauxite, 29A
bawl, 19C

bay, 16F
bazaar, 51B
beacon, 38D
beagle, 4B
beanbag, 34C
beanstalk, 24E
bear, 2I
bearded, 23B
bearing, 5R
beautify, 30E
because of, 39B
beckon, 10F
becoming, 50E
bedclothes, 17C
bedlam, 55B
bedrock, 29B
bedroll, 30F
bedspread, 30F
beech, 24B
beefsteak, 6E
beeline, 32D
beer, 6H
beeswax, 4M
beet, 6J
before now, 7G
before that, 7G
beforehand, 7G
behalf, 33D
behold, 53B
beige, 58A
being, 50A
belch, 19C
belief, 5N
belle, 9B
bellhop, 1Z
bellow, 19C
beloved, 26C
benefit, 33D
beret, 17D
berg, 16A
beriberi, 37B
berth, 16I
beryllium, 29A
beset, 33B
bestow, 2I
beta, 35C

betray, 10B
beverage, 6H
bevy, 25B
beyond, 14K
bias, 10E
bibliography, 15C
biceps, 23F
bid, 10F, 42C
bighorn, 4E
billboard, 15F
billfold, 28F
billion, 3H
bin, 22A
binary, 3G
bind, 22G
binoculars, 8K
biography, 15C
biologist, 1L
biology, 1L
birch, 24B
birthmark, 23B
birthplace, 18A
biscuit, 6D
bisect, 2W
bishop, 1W
bison, 4E
bitterness, 5E, 6L
bizarre, 55A
blab, 10A
blackbird, 4J
blacken, 38C, 41A
blackhead, 23B
blacksmith, 1N
blade, 8F
blank, 55B
blare, 19A
blast, 2S
blaze, 52C
bleach, 41C
bleacher, 30D
bleak, 41A, 55B
bleat, 19D
blemish, 23B
blight, 40D
blimp, 11D
blind, 37B

184

coppersmith, 1N
cord, 8H
core, 12B
cork, 22B
cornbread, 6D
corncob, 6J
cornerstone, 22D
cornet, 47C
cornhusk, 24E
cornmeal, 6G
cornstalk, 24E
cornstarch, 6G
cornucopia, 30E
corp, 25D
corporal, 1J
corpse, 54A
correspondence, 15F
corridor, 30A
corrode, 29D
corrugate, 2R
corrupt, 26D
corsage, 17G
cosmetics, 17G
cosmos, 20H, 55B
costly, 28E
cot, 30D
cottage, 21B
cottonseed, 24D
cottontail, 4E
cottonwood, 24B
couch, 30D
cougar, 4B
cough, 19C
council, 25E
councilman, 1C
councilwoman, 1C
counsel, 10G
counselor, 1I
countdown, 7D
countenance, 23C
counter, 30D
counterclockwise, 2X
counterfeit, 27A
countless, 3G
countryhouse, 21B
countryman, 9I

countryside, 20F
countrywoman, 9I
couple, 3G
coupon, 28C
courageous, 13N
courteous, 13A
courtesy, 13A
courthouse, 21I
courtroom, 21I
courtyard, 20G
cousin, 9N
cove, 16F, 20C
covey, 25B
coward, 9G
cowherd, 25B
cowhide, 4L
cowlick, 23B
cowslip, 24D
coy, 13L
coyote, 4B
crackle, 19E
cradle, 30D
craftsman, 1A
crag, 20D
cramp, 2R
crane, 4J
crankshaft, 8B
cranny, 20C
crate, 22A
crater, 20C
crave, 5Q
crayfish, 4I
craze, 17A
creak, 19E
crease, 17I
create, 12D, 22F
creative, 12K
credit, 28A
creed, 12L
crescendo, 19A
crescent, 32B
crest, 20D
crevice, 20C
crew, 25B
crib, 30D
crime, 26A

criminal, 9G
crimson, 58A
cringe, 5C
crinkle, 2R
cripple, 33B, 37E
crisis, 40D
crisscross, 32D
critical, 26C
criticism, 10B
criticize, 10B
croak, 19D
crochet, 17I
crock, 8M
crook, 9G
croquet, 34B
crossbar, 22D
crossbones, 9F
crossbow, 8N
crosscut, 8G
crosspiece, 22D
crossroad, 11H
crossword, 34F
crotch, 23G
crouch, 2Q
croup, 37B
crowbar, 8E
crucial, 26C
crude, 12K
cruelty, 5F
cruise, 11G
crumb, 3F
crumble, 2R
crumple, 2R
crunch, 19E
crush, 33A
crutch, 37F
crystal, 29B
cubbyhole, 22A
cubic, 32C
cuckoo, 4J
cud, 4L
cuddle, 44B
cue, 10E
cuff, 17B
cult, 25C
cultivate, 29F

cultivation, 29F
culture, 25C
culvert, 22D
cumulate, 25A
cumulonimbus, 40C
cumulus, 40C
cuneiform, 35C
cunning, 13M
cupboard, 30D
curb, 30C
curd, 6F
cure, 33D
curfew, 15H
curiosity, 12F
current, 7G, 16F
curriculum, 25A
curse, 10B
curvature, 32B
cushion, 30F
cuspid, 23D
custodian, 1R
custody, 36C
custom, 12L
customary, 7K, 42A
cut glass, 30E
cuticle, 23F
cutlass, 8N
cutoff, 8G
cutter, 11E
cycle, 7D
cyclone, 40B
cylinder, 32B
cymbal, 47C
czar, 1C

D

dab, 44A
dagger, 8N
dainty, 43D
dale, 20C
dam, 16I
damage, 33A
dame, 9B
damn, 10B
dandruff, 23B
dandy, 26C
dangle, 2B
dapple, 58A
daredevil, 1D
darken, 38C, 41A
darling, 9E
dart, 8N
data, 3H
date, 7B
daub, 41A
dawn, 7C
daybreak, 7C
daydream, 12E
daylight, 38A
daze, 12E
dazzle, 38B
deacon, 1W
deadline, 2E
deadly, 33B
deaf, 37B
deafening, 19A
dean, 1I
death, 54A

deathbed, 54A
debate, 10B
debris, 41A
debt, 28B
debut, 51B
decade, 7D
decay, 6K
deceit, 10B
deceive, 10B
decent, 26A
deciduous, 57B
decimal, 3H
declaration, 10A
declare, 10C
decline, 10B
decor, 30D
decorate, 30E
decoration, 30E
decoy, 12G
decrease, 3G
decree, 10G
dedicate, 12J
deduct, 3G
deed, 2E, 15H, 51A
deepen, 32F
defeat, 36D
defend, 33D
defense, 34C
defensive, 56B
defer, 2B
defile, 41A
define, 12I
definite, 42C
definitely, 31A
definition, 12I
deflate, 32G
deflect, 2N
deft, 12K
defy, 10B
degree, 3E
deject, 5I
delay, 2B
delegate, 1C
delicate, 57B
delightful, 26C
delightfully, 31D

equal, 27A
equality, 27A
equally, 27B
equation, 49C
equilateral, 32C
equilibrium, 55B
equip, 8A
equivalent, 27A
erect, 32H
erode, 33A
err, 26B
error, 26A
erupt, 2S
escort, 33D
essay, 15C
essence, 12B, 26C
essential, 26C
essentially, 31A
establish, 22F
establishment, 21A
estate, 21B
estimate, 12D
estuary, 16F
etch, 15I
eternal, 7K
eternity, 7F
eucalyptus, 24B
evaporate, 16B
evaporation, 16D
event, 51A
eventual, 7H
eventually, 7H
evergreen, 24B
everlasting, 7K
evidence, 12D
evident, 42A
evidently, 31A
evolve, 54B
exaggerate, 10B
exaggeration, 10B
examination, 10F, 12C
example, 27A
excavate, 8G
exceed, 3G
excel, 36D
excellent, 26C

except, 27D
except for, 27D
exceptional, 26C
excerpt, 15C
excess, 3G
exchange, 36A
exclamation, 10A
exclamatory, 35B
exclude, 5P
execute, 33B
exercise, 34D
exhale, 60D
exhaust, 32G
exhausted, 37C
exhaustion, 37C
exhibit, 10C
exist, 54A
existence, 54A
expand, 2S
expanse, 20A
expansion, 2S
expect, 5Q
expectant, 13F
expedition, 2G
expense, 28B
expensive, 28E
experience, 51A
experimentation, 12C
expert, 9L
explode, 2S
exploration, 2G
explorer, 1L
explosion, 2S
explosive, 8N
exponent, 49C
export, 2I
expose, 10H
express, 10C
expression, 10A
exquisite, 43C
extend, 32F
extensive, 3G
exterior, 14H
external, 14H
extinct, 54A
extinguish, 2F, 33A

extinguisher, 52E
extract, 36E
extraordinary, 26C
extreme(ly), 3K
eyeball, 23E
eyebrow, 23E
eyelash, 23E
eyelid, 23E
eyepiece, 8K
eyeshade, 17D
eyesight, 23E
eyesore, 41A

F
fable, 15B
fabric, 17K
fabulous, 26C
faction, 25B
factor, 3F
fad, 17A
fade, 38C
Fahrenheit, 52A

G

gadget, 8A
gag, 5K
gaggle, 25B
gain, 28A
gait, 48A
galaxy, 20H
gale, 40B
gallant, 13N
gallery, 21F
gallop, 4O
gamble, 42C
gamesman, 9L
gander, 4J
gang, 25B
gangplank, 11F
gap, 20C
gape, 53B
garb, 17A
gardenia, 24D
gargle, 6M
garland, 17G
garlic, 6G
garment, 17A
garnish, 6B
garrison, 21C
garter, 17E
gash, 37E
gatekeeper, 1Z
gatepost, 30C
gateway, 30C
gauge, 3C
gaunt, 43A
gauntlet, 17E
gauze, 17K
gawky, 43A
gazelle, 4E
gear, 8B
gee, 10K
gel, 57C
gelatin, 6G
gem, 29B

gene, 54A
general, 7K
general(ly), 3J
generate, 22F
generation, 7D
generator, 8B
generous, 13A
genesis, 2C
genetic, 54A
genie, 9F
genius, 9L
gentleman, 9C
gentlemen, 9C
gentlewoman, 9B
genuine, 26A
geographer, 1L
geographic, 20B
geographical, 20B
geography, 1L
geological, 20B
geologist, 1L
geology, 1L
geometry, 49A
geranium, 24D
Germany, 18B
getaway, 36B
geyser, 16F
ghastly, 26D
ghetto, 18A
ghostly, 26D
ghoul, 9F
giddy, 13O
gill, 4L
gimmick, 34E
gin, 6H
ginger, 6G
girlfriend, 9E
glacier, 16A
glade, 20E
gladiator, 1T
glamour, 17A
glance, 53B
gland, 23H
glare, 53B
glassware, 8M
glaze, 22F

gleam, 38A
glean, 12G
glee, 5K
glen, 20C
glider, 11D
glimmer, 38A
glimpse, 53B
glint, 38A
glisten, 38B
glitter, 38B
global, 20H
glockenspiel, 47C
gloom, 5H, 38C
glorious, 26C
glory, 42A
gloss, 38A
glow, 38B
glower, 53B
glowworm, 4K
glucose, 6B
gnash, 8G
gnat, 4K
gnaw, 6M
gneiss, 29A
goal, 34C
goalkeeper, 1D
gob, 3F
goblet, 8M
goblin, 9F
godchild, 9N
goddaughter, 9N
godfather, 9N
godmother, 9N
godson, 9N
goggles, 17D
golden haired, 58A
goldenrod, 24D
goldsmith, 1N
golf, 34B
gong, 19B
goo, 16E
gorge, 6M
gorgeous, 43C
gorilla, 4G
gossip, 9G
govern, 10G

grace, 13A
graceful, 43A
gracious, 13A
graduate, 1I, 2E
graduation, 51B
graft, 2V
gram, 3E
grammar, 35A
grandnephew, 9N
grandstand, 21G
granite, 29B
grant, 28A
grapevine, 24E
graphite, 29A
grasp, 44B
grasshopper, 4K
grassland, 20F
grate, 8G
grateful, 13A
gratitude, 5O
grave, 13H
gravedigger, 1F
gravel, 29B
gravestone, 21M
graveyard, 20G
gravity, 2K
graze, 4O
grease, 8C
greatly, 3K
greatness, 3A
greed, 5Q
greenery, 24A
greenhouse, 21K
Greenland, 18B
grenade, 8N
grey-headed, 58A
greyhaired, 58A
greyhound, 4B
griddle, 8D
grief-stricken, 5H
grieve, 5H
grill, 6K
grim, 26D
grime, 41A
grind, 8G
grindstone, 29B

grip, 8I, 44B
gripe, 10B
grit, 13N
groan, 19C
groggy, 37C
groom, 9N
groove, 20C
grope, 44A
gross, 49B
grotesque, 55A
groundwork, 22F
grout, 22D
grove, 20E
grower, 1F
grub, 29F
grudge, 5M
gruel, 6D
grueling, 56A
gruff, 5G
grunt, 19D
guaranty, 10I
guardhouse, 21C
guardian, 9N
guardroom, 21C
guide, 33D
guidebook, 15C
guideline, 10G
guillotine, 8N
guilt, 5D
guilty, 5D
guinea, 28C
gulch, 20C
gulf, 16F
gulley, 20C
gumdrop, 6C
gunfighter, 9G
gunpowder, 8N
gunshot, 8N
gunsmith, 1N
gunwale, 11F
guppy, 4H
gurgle, 19E
gush, 16B
gusher, 16F
gust, 40B
gusto, 43A

gut, 23H
gutter, 30C
guy, 9C
guzzle, 6M
gym, 21G
gymnast, 1D
gypsy, 9H

H

habitat, 21B
hack, 8G
had best, 50D
hadn't, 46A
hag, 9F
hail, 16A
hailstone, 16A
hailstorm, 40B
hairline, 23B
hairpin, 17G
hale, 37A
halfback, 1D
halfway, 14F

hither, 14G
hitherto, 7G
hoard, 36F
hoarse, 19A
hobble, 48A
hobby, 34A
hobo, 9H
hockey, 34B
hoe, 8E
hog, 4E
hogan, 21B
hogshead, 22A
hoist, 2O
holdup, 36E
holiday, 51B
Holland, 18B
holler, 19C
holly, 24D
holy, 13J
homecoming, 2I
homeland, 18A
homely, 43C
homemade, 30E
homer, 34C
homespun, 17K
homestead, 21B
homeward, 14K
homograph, 35B
homonym, 35B
homophone, 35B
honest, 26A
honestly, 31A
honesty, 26A
honeycomb, 4M
honeydew, 6I
honeymoon, 51B
honeysuckle, 24D
honorable, 26A
hoof, 4L
hoofbeat, 19D
hookup, 2V
hoot, 19D
hopeful, 13E
hopeless, 5N
hopper, 22A
horde, 25B

horizon, 14B
horizontal, 14C
hornet, 4K
horrible, 26D
horrify, 5C
horror, 5B
horseback, 4O
horsecar, 11A
horseflesh, 4E
horseless, 4O
horseman, 1D
horseplay, 34D
horsewhip, 33B
horsewoman, 1D
hospitality, 13A
host, 9C
hostage, 9G
hostess, 9B
hostile, 5E
hothead, 9G
hothouse, 21K
hourglass, 7B
housefly, 4K
household, 9N
housekeeper, 1Z
housetop, 30B
hovel, 21B
hover, 2B
howdy, 10K
however, 27D
hub, 11F
hubbub, 5J
huckleberry, 24D
huddle, 25B
hue, 58A
huff, 5E
humble, 28E
humid, 16B
hummingbird, 4J
humorous, 13I
hump, 23B
humpback, 4H
humus, 29E
hunch, 12D
hunchback, 9G
hunter, 1F

hurdle, 34C
hurl, 2J
hurricane, 40B
hush, 19A
husk, 24E
hustle, 7J
hutch, 30D
hybrid, 25A
hydraulic, 16C
hydrochloric, 59B
hydroelectric, 61A
hydrogen, 59A
hyena, 4B
hygiene, 41B
hymn, 15D
hymnal, 15C
hyperbole, 10B
hyphen, 35A
hypnosis, 12E

I

iceberg, 16A
icebox, 8D
icebreaker, 11E
icecap, 16A
icehouse, 21A
icy, 40E
ideal, 12L
ideally, 31A
identical, 27A
identify, 53B
idiom, 35A
idle, 13C
idol, 9K
if only, 39B
if...then, 39B
igloo, 21B
ignite, 52C
ignorance, 12K
ignorant, 12K
ignore, 53B
illness, 37A
illuminate, 38B
illustrate, 15I
illustration, 15E
image, 53A
imagination, 12A
imaginative, 12K
imitate, 27A
imitation, 27A
immaculate, 41B
immediate, 7J
immediately, 7I
immense, 3A
immune, 56B
imp, 9F
impact, 39A
impair, 37C
impatient, 13F
impertinent, 5G
implement, 8E
import, 2I
impose, 5I
impress, 39A
impression, 5A
impressive, 26C

imprison, 13D
improve, 33D
improvise, 12D
impulse, 5A
impurity, 41A
in addition, 27B
in any case, 27D
in any event, 27D
in comparison, 27D
in particular, 3J
in that, 39B
in that case, 39B
in the beginning, 7G
in the least bit, 3J
in the meantime, 7I
in the slightest, 3J
inactive, 13C
incense, 5E, 60B
incentive, 39A
incident, 51A
incline, 32H
include, 2V
income, 28A
incoming, 14H
incomplete, 55A
incorrect, 26A
incorrectly, 31F
increase, 3G
incredible, 26C
incredibly, 31C
incubate, 54A
indefinite, 38E
indent, 15I
independence, 13D
independent, 13D
Indianapolis, 18D
indicate, 10C
indication, 12D
indicator, 12D
indigo, 58A
individual, 9A
induce, 39A
industrious, 13B
industry, 1K
inert, 2B
inertia, 2T

inevitably, 31C
inexpensive, 28E
infant, 9D
infantry, 25D
infect, 37E, 41A
infection, 37A
infer, 12D
inferior, 26D
inferno, 52C
influence, 10E, 39A
influenza, 37B
inform, 10C
informal, 17J
infrequent, 7K
infringe, 5I
inhabit, 54A
inhabitant, 9I
inhale, 60B
inherit, 36E
initial, 7G
initiate, 39A
initiation, 2C
inject, 2K
injure, 33B
injury, 37A
inkstand, 15G
inkwell, 15G
inland, 14H, 16H
inlet, 16F
inning, 34C
innocence, 26A
innocent, 26A
inoculate, 37F
inquire, 10F
inscription, 15A
insert, 2K
insignificant, 26D
insist, 10G
insofar, 3J
inspect, 12C
inspection, 12C
inspector, 1J
inspire, 10D
install, 22F
installation, 21A
instance, 51A

instant, 7C, 7J
instinct, 12L
institute, 25E
instruct, 12G
instruction, 10G, 12G
instructor, 1I
insulate, 52B
insulation, 52B
insulator, 52B
insult, 10B
insurance, 28A
insure, 28D
intake, 14H
integer, 3H
intellect, 12K
intelligence, 12K
intelligent, 12K
intelligible, 12K
intend, 12D
intense(ly), 3K
intensity, 19A
intent, 39A
inter, 54A
interfere, 5I
interior, 14H
intern, 1U
internal, 14H
international, 25C
interpret, 10J, 12I
interrogative, 35B
interrupt, 2B
interruption, 2B
intersect, 2V
intersection, 11H
interval, 7D
interview, 10F
intestine, 23H
intricate, 55B
intrigue, 12F
introduce, 2C
introduction, 2C
introductory, 7G
invade, 33C
invalid, 9G
invaluable, 26C
invasion, 33C

invent, 12D
invention, 12D
inventor, 1L
inventory, 25A
invert, 2X
invertebrate, 4A
invest, 28D
investigate, 12C
investigation, 12C
invoice, 25A
involve, 2V
inward, 14H
iodine, 37F
ion, 61B
Iran, 18B
iridescent, 58A
ironically, 31C
ironwork, 30E
irregular, 7K
irrigate, 29F
irrigation, 29F
irritable, 5G
irritate, 5E
is bound to, 50D
isolate, 5P
isometric, 32C
isotope, 61B
Israel, 18B
issue, 15C
isthmus, 16G
italicize, 15I
italics, 35C
Italy, 18B
itch, 37C
ivory, 4L

J

jab, 44A
jabber, 10A
jack, 8E
jackal, 4B
jackass, 4E
jackknife, 8F
Jacksonville, 18D
jade, 29B
jailbird, 9G
jalopy, 11A
January, 7E
jamb, 30B
jangle, 19E
janitor, 1R
Japan, 18B
javelin, 8N
jaw, 23D
jawbone, 23J
jazz, 47B
jealous, 5M
jealousy, 5M
jeer, 10B
jellyfish, 4I
jeopardy, 56B
jersey, 17C
jest, 5K
jewel, 29B
jewelry, 17G
jiffy, 7J
jig, 47B
jinx, 42C

jitter, 2L
jog, 34D, 48A
jogging, 34D
jolt, 2N
johnnycake, 6D
jot, 15I
jounce, 2N
journal, 15C
jubilant, 5K
judgement, 12J
jug, 22A
juggle, 2L
juggler, 1H
jumble, 2L
jumbo, 3A
junior, 9C
junk, 41A
junkyard, 41A
Jupiter, 20H
justice, 26A
justly, 31F
jut, 2S
jute, 24D
juvenile, 9D

K

Kansas City, 18D
kayak, 11E
keen, 32E
keg, 22A
kelp, 24E
kerchief, 17G
kernel, 6J
kettle, 8M
kettledrum, 47C
keyboard, 47C
keyhole, 8H
keynote, 12B
khaki, 17K
kid, 9D
kidnap, 36E
kidney, 23H
kiln, 8D
kilogram, 3E
kilometer, 3E
kimono, 17C
kindhearted, 13A
kindle, 52C
kinetic, 2A
kink, 32B
kitchenware, 8M
knack, 5R
knapsack, 22A
knead, 6K, 44A
knicknack, 30E
knight, 1C
knit, 17I
knob, 8I
knockout, 34C
knoll, 20D
knothole, 24C
knuckle, 23F
krypton, 59A

L

lab, 21F
labor, 1d
laboratory, 21F
laborer, 1A
lack, 3G
lacquer, 58B
lacrosse, 34B
ladle, 8M
lag, 2B
lagoon, 16F
lair, 4M
lakeside, 16G
lame, 37B
lamppost, 38D
lance, 8N
landholder, 1B
landlady, 1B
landlord, 1B
landmark, 21M
landowner, 1B
landslide, 2P, 40D
lanky, 43D
Lansing, 18D
lantern, 38D
lapse, 2F, 26A

lard, 6E
largely, 3J
lariat, 8H
lark, 4J
larkspur, 24D
laser, 38D
lash, 44A
lass, 9B
latch, 8H
lately, 7G
lateral, 14C
latex, 24C
lather, 41C
latitude, 3D
latter, 7H
lattice, 30B
latticework, 30B
launch, 11G
launder, 41B
laurel, 24B
lava, 29A
lavender, 58A
lawbreaker, 9G
lawful, 26A
lawless, 26A
lawmaking, 25C
lawnmower, 8F
lax, 13C
layoff, 1d
layout, 12B
leach, 16B
leadership, 10G
league, 25E
leap, 48D
lease, 28D, 36A
leash, 4N
lecture, 10A
ledge, 30C
leftover, 3G
legacy, 28A
legal, 26A
legend, 15B
legendary, 42A
legible, 15I
legion, 25D
legislative, 25C

legislature, 25C
legume, 6B
leisure, 51B
lend, 36A
lengthen, 32F
lens, 8K
lest, 39B
letdown, 5H
letup, 2R
lever, 8E
levy, 28B
liable, 42C
liar, 9G
liberal, 13A
liberty, 13D
license, 10G
lichen, 24E
licorice, 6C
lifelong, 7D
lifesaver, 1D
lifesaving, 26C
lifetime, 7A
ligament, 23J
lightbulb, 38D
lighten, 38B
lightness, 38A
lightweight, 3A
likeness, 27A
likewise, 27B
lily, 24D
limbs, 23A
lime, 6I
limelight, 42A
limerick, 15D
limestone, 29B
limp, 48A
linear, 32D
linen, 17K
liner, 11E
linger, 2B
lingerie, 17A
lining, 17B
link, 2V
linoleum, 30E
linseed, 24D
lioness, 4B

lipstick, 17G
liquor, 6H
lisp, 35A
listless, 13C
literally, 31A
literature, 15B
litmus, 59A
litter, 41A
livelihood, 1A
lively, 13B
liver, 23H
livestock, 4A
livid, 58A
llama, 4E
loam, 29E
loan, 36A
loaves, 6D
lob, 44A
lobby, 30A
lobe, 23E
lobster, 4I
local, 14K
locate, 36F
location, 20A
locket, 17G
locksmith, 1N
locomotive, 11A
locust, 24B
lodestone, 29A
lodge, 21B
loft, 30A
logger, 1F
logic, 12H
logical, 12K
loneliness, 5H
longitude, 3D
longstanding, 7K
longtime, 7K
loom, 53B
loot, 36E
lope, 48A
lopsided, 27C
lord, 1C
lore, 12G
loss, 28B, 36D
lotion, 41C

loudspeaker, 19B
Louisville, 18D
lounge, 2B
lover, 9E
lowland, 20F
loyal, 13N
loyalty, 13N
lozenge, 6C
lubricate, 8C
lug, 2K
luggage, 22A
lukewarm, 52A
lull, 19A
lumber, 22C
lumberjack, 1F
lumberman, 1F
lumberyard, 21E
luminous, 38A
lunar, 20H
lung, 23H
lunge, 48D
lurch, 2N, 48D
lure, 10E
lurk, 48B
lush, 3G
luster, 38A
lute, 47C
luxury, 28E
lye, 41C
lyre, 47C
lyric, 15D

M
ma'am, 9B
macaroni, 6D
machinery, 8A
madam, 9B
madame, 9B
magenta, 58A
magical, 34E
magician, 1H
magma, 29A
magnificent, 26C
magnify, 2S
maiden, 9B
mainland, 16G
mainstay, 11F
mainstream, 42A
maintain, 36C
maintenance, 22F
maize, 6J
majestic, 43C
majesty, 9A
majority, 3G
makeshift, 57B
malaria, 37B
mallard, 4J
malt, 6J
mammoth, 3A
manage, 10G
manager, 1B
mandolin, 47C
mane, 4L
manganese, 29A
mangle, 33A
mania, 5O
manicure, 41B
mankind, 9A

manor, 21B
mansion, 21B
mantel, 30B
mantelpiece, 30B
mantis, 4K
mantle, 17F
manual, 15C
manufacture, 22F
manufacturer, 1P
manure, 29E
manuscript, 15C
maple, 24B
mar, 33A
marathon, 34A
marble, 29B
mare, 4E
marigold, 24D
marine, 11G
marines, 25D
marketplace, 28F
marksman, 1D
markswoman, 1D
marmalade, 6C
maroon, 58A
marriage, 2V
Mars, 20H
marsh, 16F
marshland, 16F
marvel, 5J
marvelous, 26C
mascot, 4A
masculine, 9C
mash, 33A
mason, 1X
mass, 25B
massacre, 33B
massage, 44A
massive, 3A
mast, 11F
master, 9C
matchbox, 52E
mate, 3G, 9E
material, 17K, 22E
math, 49A
mathematician, 1L
mathematics, 49A

momentary, 7K
monarch, 1C
monastery, 21I
moneybag, 28F
monitor, 53B
monk, 1W
monogram, 15A
monopoly, 36C
monsoon, 40B
monstrous, 3A
Montgomery, 18D
monument, 21M
mood, 5A
moonbeam, 38D
moor, 20B
moral, 26A
more or less, 3J
moreover, 27B
morgue, 21H
moron, 9G
morrow, 7F
morsel, 3F
mortal, 54A
mortar, 22D
mortgage, 28B
mortuary, 21H
mosaic, 47D
motion, 2A
motionless, 2B
motive, 39A
motorcar, 11A
motto, 15F
mount, 2O
mountainous, 20B
mountainside, 20D
mourn, 5H
mouthful, 3E
mouthpiece, 47C
movement, 2A
movie, 47A
muck, 16E
mucus, 23I
muddle, 55B
muff, 26B
muffin, 6D
muffle, 2F

muffler, 17G
mug, 8M
muggy, 40E
multiple, 49B
multiplication, 49D
multiply, 49D
mumble, 19C
mummy, 54A
munch, 6M
municipal, 20B
mural, 47D
murder, 33B
murky, 38E
murmur, 19C
muscle, 23J
muscular, 43A
musical, 47B
musician, 1G
musket, 8N
muskrat, 4F
mustache, 23B
mustang, 4E
mustard, 6G
muster, 25A
mustn't, 46A
mute, 37B
mutt, 4B
mutton, 6E
muzzle, 4N
mysterious, 42C
mystify, 12G
myth, 15B
mythology, 12L

N
nab, 44B
nag, 10B
naive, 12K
naked, 17J
namely, 27B
nape, 23A
napkin, 30F
narcotic, 37F
narrator, 1E
Nashville, 18D
nasty, 41A
natal, 54A
national, 25C
nationwide, 18A
native, 9I
naturally, 31C
nature, 40A
naughty, 13M
nausea, 37C
naval, 11G
navigate, 11G
navy, 25D
necessary, 26C
nectar, 6H
needy, 28E
negative, 26D
neglect, 5P
negotiate, 10A
neigh, 19D
neither...nor, 27D
neon, 59A
Neptune, 20H
nerve, 23J

network, 25A
neutral, 55B
neutron, 61B
nevermore, 7K
nevertheless, 27D
New Orleans, 18D
newborn, 9D
newcomer, 9I
newscarrier, 1b
newscaster, 1E
newspaperman, 1E
newsreel, 47A
nibble, 6M
nick, 33A
nigh, 14K
nightcap, 17D
nightfall, 7C
nightmare, 12E
nightshirt, 17C
nip, 44B
nitrate, 59A
nitrogen, 59A
noble, 13A
nobleman, 1C
nomadic, 2G
nominate, 51C
nonetheless, 27D
nonfiction, 15B
nonliving, 54A
noodles, 6D
nook, 30D
noonday, 7C
noose, 8N
norm, 42A
normal, 42A
northeastern, 14E
northerly, 14E
northernmost, 14E
northland, 14E
northward, 14E
northwestern, 14E
nostril, 23E
notably, 3K
notation, 35C
notch, 20C
noteworthy, 26C

notify, 10C
notwithstanding, 27D
nourish, 33D
nourishment, 6B
novel, 15C
novice, 9L
now that, 7G, 39B
nowadays, 7I
nozzle, 16C
nuclei, 61B
nucleus, 61B
nude, 17J
nudge, 44A
nugget, 29B
nuisance, 9G
null, 32G
numb, 37C
numeration, 3H
numerous, 3G
nun, 1W
nursemaid, 1c
nursery, 30A
nutbrown, 58A
nutcracker, 8M
nutmeg, 6G
nutrition, 6B
nutshell, 6J
nuzzle, 44B
nylon, 17K
nymph, 4C

O

oar, 11F
oasis, 24A
oats, 6J
obedience, 13N
obedient, 13D
objection, 10B
objective, 12B
oboe, 47C
observatory, 21F
observe, 53B
observer, 53A
obsidian, 29A
obstacle, 2F
obstinate, 13H
obstruct, 2F
obtain, 36E
obverse, 14F
obvious, 42A
obviously, 31A
occasion, 51A
occasional, 7K
occupation, 1A
occupy, 36C
occur, 2D
occurrence, 51A
octagon, 32C
octave, 47B
octopus, 4I
oddly, 31C
odor, 60B
offend, 5E, 33B
offense, 34C
offhand, 7J
officeholder, 1C
official, 1C
offset, 55B

paradise, 18A
paraffin, 52E
paragraph, 15C
parakeet, 4J
parallel, 27A
parallelogram, 32C
paralyze, 33B, 37E
parasite, 4K
parasol, 17G
parcel, 22A
parchment, 15G
pardon, 5O
pare, 8G
parenthesis, 35A
parkway, 11H
parliament, 25C
parlor, 30A
parole, 36B
parsley, 6G
parson, 1W
partial, 3G
participate, 10D
participle, 35B
particle, 3F
particular, 3G
particularly, 3J
partly, 3J
partner, 9E
partnership, 25E
passageway, 11H
passenger, 9H, 11G
passion, 5J
passport, 15H
password, 35B
pasteboard, 15G
pastel, 15G
pasteurize, 41B
pastime, 51B
pastor, 1W
pastry, 6C
pastrycook, 1N
patent, 42A
patience, 13F
patient, 13F
patio, 20G
patriarch, 9N

patriotic, 13N
patrol, 25D
patrolman, 1J
patty, 6C
pause, 2B
pave, 22F
pavement, 22D
payment, 28B
payroll, 28C
peace, 33C
peaceful, 5L
peacetime, 7A
peak, 14I
peal, 19A
pearl, 29B
peasant, 9M
peat, 29E
pebble, 29C
pecan, 6J
peck, 8G
peculiar, 55A
peddle, 28D
peddler, 1M
pedestal, 22D
pedestrian, 42A
pedigree, 9N
peer, 9E, 53B
peg, 8H
pellet, 8N
pelt, 4L
pemmican, 6E
penal, 33B
pendant, 17G
penetrate, 16B
penicillin, 37F
peninsula, 16G
penmanship, 15I
pennant, 30E
pentagon, 32C
Peoria, 18D
pep, 13B
peppermint, 6C
per, 49D
perceive, 53B
percent, 49B
percentage, 49B

percussion, 47C
perfectly, 3K
perform, 47A
performance, 47A
performer, 1H
perfume, 17G, 60B
peril, 56B
perilous, 56B
perish, 54A
perishable, 57B
permanent, 7K
permit, 10G
perpendicular, 14C
persecute, 33B
persist, 7K
personality, 5R
perspiration, 23I
perspire, 23K
persuade, 10E
petite, 3A
petition, 10E
petrify, 5C
petroleum, 8C
petticoat, 17C
petty, 26D
petunia, 24D
pew, 30D
phantom, 9F
pharmacy, 21D
pheasant, 4J
Philadelphia, 18D
philosophy, 12L
Phoenix, 18D
phonetic, 35C
phonograph, 8D
phosphate, 59A
phosphorus, 29A
photo, 47D
photograph, 47D
photographer, 1G
photography, 47D
phrase, 35B
phylum, 25B
physical, 23A
physician, 1U
piccolo, 47C

picker, 1F
pickle, 6J
pickpocket, 9G
pickup, 11A
piecemeal, 3J
pierce, 8G
pigment, 58A
pigskin, 17K
pigsty, 4M
pigtail, 23B
pill, 37F
pillar, 22C
pillbox, 22A
pimple, 23B
pinafore, 17C
pinch, 3E, 44B
pineapple, 6I
ping, 19E
pinnacle, 14I
pinpoint, 36F
pinto, 4E
pinwheel, 2X
pipeline, 22D
pistol, 8N
piston, 8B
pit, 20C
pitch, 19A
pitchfork, 8E
pitfall, 56B
pith, 24C
pitiful, 5H
Pittsburgh, 18D
pity, 5L
pixy, 9F
plague, 37A
plaid, 17K
planetarium, 21F
plank, 22C
plantation, 21L
plaque, 30E
plaster, 22D
platform, 8J
platter, 8M
platypus, 4E
playfellow, 9E
playmate, 9E

playroom, 30A
plaza, 20G
plea, 10I
plead, 10E
pledge, 10I
pliers, 8E
plod, 48A
plop, 19E
plot, 20A, 47A
pluck, 44B
plum, 6I
plumb, 32H
plumber, 1X
plume, 4L
plump, 43D
plunder, 36E
plunge, 2P
plunk, 19E
plural, 3G
plush, 17K
Pluto, 20H
plywood, 22C
poach, 6K
pock, 23B
pocketbook, 28F
pocketknife, 8F
pod, 24D, 25B
poet, 1E
poetic, 15D
poetry, 15B
pointer, 8J
poison, 37E
poisonous, 33B
poker, 34F
polar, 20B
polecat, 4E
policy, 15H
polio, 37B
polish, 41B
political, 25C
politician, 1C
politics, 1K
polka, 47B
poll, 10F
pollinate, 54A
pollination, 54A

pollute, 41A
pollution, 41A
polo, 34B
polygon, 32C
pompom, 17B
poncho, 17F
ponder, 12A
poodle, 4B
poorhouse, 21C
pope, 1W
popover, 6C
popular, 42A
populate, 54A
porcelain, 22D
porcupine, 4F
pore, 23B
pork, 6E
porous, 57A
porpoise, 4H
porridge, 6D
port, 16I
portal, 30A
porter, 1V
porthole, 11F
portion, 3F
Portland, 18D
portrait, 47D
portray, 53A
portrayal, 53A
pose, 48E
posh, 28E
position, 14A
posse, 25B
possess, 36C
possession, 36C
possessive, 5M
possibly, 31B
postage, 28C
postmark, 15A
postmaster, 1b
postpone, 2B
posture, 48E
potassium, 29A
potbelly, 43D
potent, 43A, 57B
potion, 37F

pulpit, 30D
puma, 4B
pumice, 29A
pun, 35B
punch, 44A
punctuate, 15I
puncture, 33A
puny, 43A
purchase, 28D
purely, 3J
purge, 41B
purify, 41B
puritan, 9I
purpose, 39A
pursue, 2H
pursuit, 2H
puss, 4B
putt, 44A
putter, 2B, 34C
putty, 22D
pygmy, 9J
pyramid, 32C

Q

quadrilateral, 32C
quail, 4J
quaint, 55A
quake, 2L
qualify, 22F, 26B
quality, 5R
quantity, 3G
quarantine, 21C
quarrel, 10B
quarterback, 1D
quartet, 25B
quartz, 29A
quill, 4L
quilt, 30F
quintet, 25B
quirk, 27C
quit, 2F
quiver, 2L
quotation, 10J
quote, 10J
quotient, 49C

R

rabbi, 1W
rabies, 37B
raccoon, 4E
racecourse, 11H
racehorse, 4E
racer, 1D
racetrack, 11H
racket, 34C
radiant, 38A
radiate, 38B
radiation, 61A
radiator, 8D
radioactive, 61A
radiobroadcast, 47A
radiophone, 19B
radium, 29A
radius, 3D
raffle, 34F
raft, 11E
rage, 5E
ragweed, 24E
raid, 33C
rail, 11H
railway, 11H
rainstorm, 40B
ram, 4E
ramble, 48A
ramp, 11H
ramshackle, 57B
rancher, 1F
random, 42C
ranger, 1F
rank, 2O
ransack, 36E
ransom, 28D
rant, 19C
rap, 44A
rape, 33B
rapid, 7J
rare, 55A
rascal, 9G
rash, 23B
rate, 2O

respiratory, 23K
respire, 60D
respond, 10F
responsibility, 13B
responsible, 13B
restless, 13F
restore, 22F
restrain, 2F
restrict, 36F
result, 39A
retail, 28D
retain, 36F
retina, 23E
retire, 1d
retort, 10F
retreat, 21C
retrieve, 2I
reveal, 10H, 53A
revenge, 5E
reverse, 2X
review, 12C
revise, 12D
revoke, 10G
revolt, 10B
revolution, 33C
revolve, 2X
revolver, 8N
Richmond, 18D
rickety, 43A
riddle, 5K
ridge, 14B, 20D
ridicule, 10B
ridiculous, 26D
rifle, 8N
rifleman, 1J
rift, 20C
rig, 8A
rightful, 26A
rigid, 57A
rigor, 13H
rim, 14B
rind, 24E
ringside, 21G
rinse, 41B
riot, 33C
rise, 2O

risk, 56B
rival, 9G
riverside, 16G
rivet, 8H
roadside, 11H
roadway, 11H
roan, 58A
robust, 37A
rocker, 30D
rodent, 4F
role, 1A
rollicking, 5K
romance, 5O
romp, 48A
rookie, 9L
roommate, 9E
roost, 4M
rosebud, 24D
roster, 25A
rot, 6K
rotate, 2X
rotation, 2X
rotor, 11F
rotten, 6L
rouge, 17G
rough, 57A
roughly, 3J
roughrider, 1F
roundabout, 14K
roundup, 25E
rouse, 12E
rout, 55B
route, 11H
routine, 12H
rover, 9H
rowboat, 11E
royal, 28E
rubbish, 41A
rubble, 29B
ruby, 29B
ruckus, 19C
rudder, 11F
ruddy, 23B
ruff, 17B
ruffian, 9G
ruffle, 17B

rugged, 43A
rumble, 33C
rummage, 12C
rumor, 10B
rump, 23A
rumple, 17I
rumpus, 19C
runaway, 9H
rung, 22D
runoff, 16F
runt, 9J
runway, 11H
rupture, 33A
rural, 20B
russet, 58A
rust, 29D
rustic, 20B
rustle, 19E
rustler, 9G
rut, 20C
rye, 6J

S

sac, 4L
sacred, 13J
sacrifice, 36B
saddlebag, 4N
safeguard, 33D
sag, 2P
sagebrush, 24E
sailboat, 11E
saint, 9F
sake, 33D
salary, 28A
salesclerk, 1M
salesman, 1M
salesperson, 1M
saleswoman, 1M
saliva, 23I
salmon, 4H
salon, 21D
saloon, 21D
saloonkeeper, 1N
Salt Lake City, 18D
salute, 44C
San Antonio, 18D
sandal, 17E
sandalwood, 22C
sandbag, 22A
sandbank, 16G
sandbox, 34F
sandman, 9F
sandpaper, 8E
sandstone, 29B
sandstorm, 40B
sane, 37A
sanitary, 41B
sanitation, 41B
sanity, 37A
Santa Fe, 18D
sash, 17G
satellite, 20H
satisfactory, 26A
Saturn, 20H
saucepan, 8M
saucy, 5G
savage, 5F
savings, 28A

savior, 9K
savor, 6L
sawdust, 3F
sawhorse, 8J
sawmill, 21E
saxophone, 47C
scab, 37E
scald, 6K
scallop, 4I
scalp, 23B
scamp, 9G
scamper, 48A
scan, 15I
scarce, 55A
scarcely, 3J
scarlet, 58A
scatterbrain, 9G
scene, 47A, 53A
scenery, 47A
scent, 60B
scepter, 17G
scheme, 12B
scholar, 9L
scholarship, 28A
schoolbook, 15C
schoolfellow, 9C
schoolgirl, 9B
schoolmaster, 1I
schoolmate, 9E
schoolmistress, 1I
schoolwork, 12C
schooner, 11E
scientific, 12K
scoff, 10B
scoop, 8G
scoot, 7J
scooter, 11A
scope, 12B
scorch, 52C
score, 15D
scorn, 5E
scornful, 5G
scoundrel, 9G
scour, 41B
scourge, 33B
scout, 53B

scowl, 60A
scrag, 43D
scramble, 2L
scrap, 3F
scraper, 8E
scrawl, 15I
scrawny, 43A
screech, 19C
screw, 8H
screwdriver, 8E
scribe, 1E
scrimp, 28D
script, 15C
scripture, 15C
scroll, 15G
scruff, 23A
scuffle, 33C
sculptor, 1G
sculpture, 47D
scum, 16E
scurry, 7J
scurvy, 37B
scuttle, 22A
scythe, 8F
seaboard, 16G
seacoast, 16G
seafood, 6B
seahorse, 4H
seam, 2V, 17B
seaman, 1V
seaplane, 11D
seaport, 16I
searchlight, 38D
seasick, 37A
Seattle, 18D
seaway, 11H
seaweed, 24E
secondhand, 7F
secrecy, 42B
secretary, 1O
secrete, 16B
sect, 25C
secure, 44B, 56B
sedan, 11A
sediment, 16E
sedimentary, 29C

seek, 5Q

seemingly, 31B

seep, 16B

segment, 3F

seldom, 7K

seller, 1M

seminary, 21F

senate, 25C

senator, 1C

senior, 9D

señor, 9C

sensation, 5A

sensible, 13K

sensibly, 31G

sensitive, 13A

sensory, 23K

separate, 27C

septic, 37D

sequence, 25A

sequin, 17G

serenade, 15D

serene, 19A

sergeant, 1J

series, 25A

seriously, 31A

sermon, 10A

serpent, 4C

serum, 37F

servant, 1Z

service, 13B

session, 25E

setting, 47A

settler, 9I

setup, 25A

severe, 13H

sewage, 41A

sewer, 22D

sex, 54A

shabby, 26D

shack, 21K

shackle, 2V

shady, 38C

shaft, 20C

shaggy, 57A

shale, 29B

shallow, 32F

shamble, 48A

shame, 5D

shampoo, 41C

shank, 23G

shanty, 21B

sharecropper, 1F

shark, 4H

sharpen, 32E

sharpshooter, 1D

shatter, 33A

shawl, 17F

sheaf, 25A

shear, 8G

sheath, 17H

sheen, 38A

sheepskin, 17K

sheer, 17J

sherbet, 6C

shield, 17H

shift, 2M

shilling, 28C

shimmer, 38B

shin, 23G

shingle, 22C

shipbuilding, 1P

shipload, 22A

shipmate, 1V

shipment, 22A

shipowner, 1V

shipshape, 43B

shipwreck, 11E

shipyard, 16I

shoddy, 26D

shoeshine, 41B

shopkeeper, 1M

shopwindow, 30B

shoreline, 16G

shortage, 3G

shortcake, 6C

shortcoming, 26A

shortcut, 11H

shorthand, 15I

shortstop, 1D

shotgun, 8N

shoulders, 23F

showboat, 11E

showdown, 33C

showman, 1H

showroom, 30A

shred, 8G

shrew, 4F

shrewd, 12K

shrewdly, 31G

shriek, 19C

shrill, 19A

shrine, 21I

shrivel, 2R

shrub, 24A

shrug, 44C

shudder, 2L

shuffle, 48A

shun, 53B

shutter, 30B

shuttle, 2I

sickle, 8F

sickness, 37A

sideboard, 30D

sideburns, 23B

sideline, 1A

sidetrack, 11H

sideways, 14C

siege, 33C

sierra, 20D

sieve, 8M

sift, 6K

sightly, 43C

sightseeing, 2G

signboard, 15F

signpost, 15F

silhouette, 32A

silicon, 29A

silkworm, 4K

silo, 20C, 21A

silt, 16E

silversmith, 1N

silverware, 8M

similar, 27A

similarity, 27A

simmer, 6K

simper, 60A

simplify, 56A

simply, 3J

simultaneously, 7I
sincere, 13B
sincerity, 13B
sine, 49B
sinew, 23J
singe, 52C
singular, 3G
sinister, 26D
sinuous, 32D
sire, 1C
siren, 19B
sissy, 9N
site, 20A
situation, 51A
sizzle, 52C
skater, 1D
skein, 17K
skeletal, 23K
sketch, 15I
skewer, 6K
ski, 34C
skid, 2M
skier, 1D
skiing, 34B
skillet, 8M
skillful, 12K
skim, 15I
skinny, 43D
skipper, 1V
skirmish, 33C
skit, 47A
skittish, 13L
skull, 23C
skylark, 4J
skylight, 38D
skyline, 32A
skyrocket, 2O
skyward, 14I
slab, 3F
slack, 13P
slacks, 17C
slam, 19E
slang, 35A
slant, 32H
slash, 8G
slat, 22C

slate, 29B
slaughter, 33B
slaveholder, 1T
slay, 33B
sledge, 8E
sleek, 43C
sleet, 16A
slender, 43D
slice, 8G
slick, 16B
slicker, 17F
slight, 43D
slightly, 3J
slim, 43D
sling, 8N, 37F
slingshot, 8N
slink, 48B
slip, 2M
slit, 8G
slither, 48B
sliver, 3F
slobber, 60C
slogan, 15F
slop, 41A
slope, 20D
sloppy, 43B
slosh, 16B
slot, 8H
slouch, 2P
slug, 4K
sluice, 16I
slum, 18A
slump, 2P
slur, 10B
slush, 16A
sly, 13M
smack, 44A
smallpox, 37B
smear, 41A
smelt, 4H
smirk, 60A
smith, 1N
smog, 16D
smokehouse, 21D
smokestack, 30B
smokey, 52D

smolder, 52C
smother, 2F
smudge, 41A
smug, 13E
smut, 52D
snag, 2J
snail, 4I
snapdragon, 24D
snapper, 4H
snapshot, 47D
snare, 4O
snarl, 19D
sneak, 48B
sneer, 60A
snicker, 19C
snip, 8G
snoop, 53B
snooze, 12E
snore, 19C, 60B
snorkel, 16B
snout, 4L
snowcap, 16A
snowshoe, 17E
snub, 53B
snuff, 33A
snug, 5L
snuggle, 44B
so far, 7G
so that, 39B
soapstone, 29A
soapsuds, 41C
sober, 13H
soccer, 34B
social, 13A
society, 25C
socket, 22A
sod, 29E
sodium, 59A
sofa, 30D
softball, 34B
soften, 57C
soggy, 16B
solar, 20H
solder, 29A
sole, 3G
solemn, 5I

stall, 4M
stallion, 4E
stamina, 54B
stammer, 19C
stampede, 4O
standard, 42A
standpoint, 14A
standstill, 2B
stanza, 15D
staple, 8H
starboard, 14E
starch, 6G
starlight, 38A
starling, 4J
starter, 8B
startle, 5C
starvation, 37B
stateroom, 30A
statesman, 1C
static, 2B
stationary, 2B
stationery, 15G
stave, 47B
stead, 33D
steadfast, 13H
steady, 55B
steak, 6E
steamboat, 11E
steamer, 11E
steamship, 11E
steamshovel, 11B
steed, 4E
steel, 29A
steep, 32H
steeple, 30B
steeplechase, 34B
stein, 8M
stellar, 20H
stench, 60B
stencil, 15I
stepladder, 8J
steppe, 20B
stereo, 8D
sterile, 41B
sterilize, 41B
stern, 13H

stevedore, 1V
stewardess, 1V
stewpan, 8M
stiffen, 57C
stifle, 2F
stigma, 15A
stile, 30B
stilt, 22D
stimulate, 39A
stimulus, 39A
sting, 4O
stingray, 4I
stingy, 13P
stink, 60B
stirrup, 4N
stitch, 17I
stock, 25A, 28C
stockade, 21C
stockman, 1F
stockyard, 4M
stoke, 52C
stole, 17F
stomp, 48C
stonecutter, 1F
stonemason, 1X
stoney, 57A
stoop, 2Q
stopper, 22B
stopwatch, 7B
storehouse, 21K
storekeeper, 1M
storyteller, 9G
stout, 43D
stovepipe, 30B
stowaway, 11G
straddle, 48E
straightforward, 13N
strain, 5D, 41B
strand, 16G
strangle, 60D
strategy, 12B
stray, 2G
streak, 41A
streamline, 22F
streetcar, 11A
strength, 43A

strengthen, 22F
stress, 10C
stretch, 34D
stricken, 37A
strict, 13H
strictly, 31A
stride, 48A
strife, 33C
strive, 1d
stroke, 44A
stroll, 48A
strongbox, 28F
stronghold, 21C
structure, 21A
struggle, 33C
strum, 44B
strut, 48A
stub, 3G
stubborn, 13H
stubby, 3A
stucco, 22D
stud, 4E
studio, 21E
stuffy, 13H
stumble, 48A
stump, 24C
stun, 33B
stunt, 34E
stupidity, 12K
stupor, 12E
sturdy, 57B
stutter, 19C
style, 17A
sub, 11E
subdue, 36D
subheading, 15A
subject, 12B
sublime, 26C
submarine, 11E
submerge, 16B
submit, 10G
subscribe, 28D
subsequently, 7H
subset, 3F
subsist, 54A
substitute, 27A

T

tab, 28B
tablecloth, 30F
tableland, 20D
tablespoon, 8M
tablet, 15G
tabletop, 30D
tableware, 8M
tack, 8H
tackle, 34C
tactful, 13A
tactics, 12H
taffy, 6C
tailor, 1N
takeoff, 2G
talc, 29A
talent, 5R
talkative, 10A
tallow, 8C
tally, 49D
talon, 4L
tambourine, 47C
tame, 5L
Tampa, 18D
tang, 6L
tangerine, 6I, 58A
tangible, 57A
tangle, 43B, 55B
tank, 22A
tanker, 11E
tannery, 21E
tapestry, 30E
tar, 22D
tardy, 7H
target, 34C
tariff, 28B
tarnish, 29D
tarpaulin, 22B
tart, 6C
tassel, 17B
tatter, 17I
taupe, 58A
taut, 57A
tawny, 58A
tax, 28B

taxation, 28B
taxidermy, 1L
taxpayer, 9I
teak, 24B
teammate, 9E
teamwork, 10D
teat, 23A
technical, 55B
technically, 31A
technician, 1X
technique, 12H
technology, 1K
tee, 34C
teen, 9D
teepee, 21B
teeter, 2L
telegram, 15F
telegraph, 10C
telegrapher, 1b
telescope, 8K
teller, 1S
telltale, 9G
temper, 5E, 27C
temperate, 52A
tempest, 40B
temple, 21I
tempo, 7J
temporary, 7K
tempt, 10E
tenant, 9I
tend, 29F
tendon, 23J
tennis, 34B
tense, 5D
tension, 5D
term, 7D
terminal, 8L, 21J
terminate, 2F
termite, 4K
terrain, 20A
terribly, 3K
terrier, 4B
terrific, 26C
terrify, 5C
territory, 20A
terry, 17K

test tube, 22A
testament, 15C
testimony, 10A
tether, 2V
text, 15C
textbook, 15C
textile, 17K
texture, 17K, 57A
thatch, 24E
thaw, 16B
theater, 21G
thee, 45A
theirs, 45B
theme, 12B
theoretically, 31B
theory, 12D
therapy, 37F
thereabout, 14K
thereabouts, 14K
thereafter, 7H
thereby, 39B
therefore, 39B
therefrom, 39B
there'll, 46C
thereof, 7I
thereon, 14I
thereto, 14G
thermal, 52A
thermostat, 8L
thesaurus, 15C
thicken, 32F
thicket, 20E
thigh, 23G
thimble, 22B
thistle, 24D
thong, 8H
thorax, 23A
thorn, 24C
thorough, 13B
thorough(ly), 3K
thou, 45A
thrash, 44A
threadlike, 32F
threat, 10B
threaten, 10B
threescore, 3H

treason, 13M
treatment, 37F
treaty, 15H
treble, 47B
trellis, 30C
tremendous, 26C
trench, 20C
Trenton, 18D
trespass, 36E
tress, 23B
trial, 10B
triangular, 32C
tribal, 25C
tribesman, 9I
tribune, 1C
tributary, 16F
tribute, 10D
trice, 3H
tricky, 13M
tricycle, 11A
trifle, 30E
trigger, 8J
trigonometry, 49A
trill, 19A
trillion, 3H
trim, 32F
trimmer, 8F
trinket, 17G
trio, 25B
triple, 3H
triumph, 36D
triumphant, 36D
trolley, 11A
trombone, 47C
troop, 25D
trooper, 1J
tropical, 20B
tropics, 20A
troublesome, 56A
trough, 22A
troupe, 25E
trousers, 17C
trout, 4H
truant, 14L
trudge, 48A

trumpet, 47C
trundle, 2I
trustworthiness, 13B
trustworthy, 13B
truth, 26A
truthfully, 31A
tryout, 47A
tuba, 47C
tuber, 24D
tuberculosis, 37B
tuck, 36F
tuft, 23B
tugboat, 11E
tumble, 2P
tumor, 23B
tuna, 4H
tundra, 20B
tungsten, 29A
tuningfork, 47C
turban, 17D
turbine, 8B
turf, 29E
turmoil, 55B
turnip, 6J
turnout, 41B
turnover, 36B
turpentine, 8C
turquoise, 29B
turtledove, 4J
tusk, 4L
tutor, 1I
tuxedo, 17A
twang, 19E
tweeze, 44B
twilight, 7C
twine, 8H
twinge, 37C
twinkle, 38B
twirl, 2X
twister, 40B
twitch, 2N
typewrite, 15I
typewriter, 15G
typhoon, 40B
typical, 42A

typically, 31C
typist, 1O
tyrant, 9G

U

udder, 23A
ugh, 10K
umpire, 1D
unattractive, 43C
unavailable, 14L
unbearable, 56A
unbroken, 55B
uncanny, 55A
uncertain, 42C
unchanged, 55B
uncomfortable, 5D
uncommon, 55A
unconscious, 12E
uncontrolled, 13O
undeniably, 31A
underbrush, 24A

wary, 13P
washbasin, 22A
washboard, 41C
washbowl, 22A
washout, 36D
washroom, 30A
washstand, 30D
washtub, 22A
wasn't, 46A
wasp, 4K
wasteful, 28E
wasteland, 20B
wastepaper, 41A
watchmaker, 1N
watchman, 1T
waterbottle, 22A
watercolor, 15I
watercress, 6D
waterfowl, 4J
waterfront, 16G
waterglass, 8M
waterline, 16F
waterlog, 16B
waterproof, 16B
watershed, 20D
waterside, 16G
waterspout, 22D
watertight, 16B
waterway, 11H
waterwheel, 16C
watt, 3E
wavelength, 38A
waver, 2L
wax, 41B
waylay, 2B
wayside, 11H
weakness, 43A
wealth, 28C
weapon, 8N
weariness, 37C
weasel, 4E
weatherman, 1E
weave, 17I
weaver, 1N
web, 25A

wedding, 2V
wedge, 8E
wee, 3A
weed, 12J
weird, 55A
welt, 37E
westernmost, 14E
westward, 14E
we've 46B
whack, 44A
whaleboat, 11E
whalebone, 4L
wham, 44A
wharf, 16I
whatever, 45D
what's, 46D
wheelchair, 30D
wheeze, 19C
whenever, 45F
whensoever, 45F
whereabouts, 14A
whereas, 27D, 39B
whereby, 39B
wherefore, 39B
where's, 46D
whereupon, 39B
wherever, 45F
wherewith, 39B
whichever, 45D
whiff, 60D
whilst, 7I
whine, 19C
whinny, 19D
whiplash, 37E
whirl, 2X
whirlwind, 40B
whisk, 7J
whiskey, 6H
whist, 34F
white cap, 16F
whitewash, 41B, 58B
whittle, 8G
whoever, 45E
wholesome, 26A
whom, 45C

whomever, 45D
whomsoever, 45E
whop, 44A
Wichita, 18D
wick, 52E
wicker, 24C
wicket, 30B
widely, 3K
wide-mouthed, 22A
widen, 32F
widespread, 42A
widow, 9B
width, 32F
wield, 44C
wigwam, 21B
wildcat, 4B
wilderness, 20B
wildfire, 52C
wildflower, 24D
willing, 13A
wilt, 2R
windblown, 43B
windbreak, 21C
windfall, 28A
windlass, 8J
windowseat, 30B
windowsill, 30B
windpipe, 23D
windshield, 11F
windstorm, 40B
wine, 6H
wingspread, 11F
wintry, 40E
wisecrack, 5K
wit, 12K
witchcraft, 34E
withdraw, 2G
wither, 2R
withhold, 36F
withstand, 54B
witness, 53A
witty, 13I
wizard, 9F
wobble, 2L
woe, 5H

wolfhound, 4B
wonderland, 18A
woodchuck, 4F
woodcraft, 47D
woodcutter, 1F
woodland, 20E
woodpile, 52E
woodshed, 21K
woodsman, 1F
woodwind, 47C
workbench, 30D
workday, 7C
workhouse, 21E
workingman, 1A
workout, 34D
workshop, 21E
worktable, 30D
worship, 10D
worthless, 26D
worthwhile, 26C
wouldn't, 46A
wrapper, 22B
wrath, 5E
wreath, 30E
wreckage, 33A
wren, 4J
wrench, 8E
wrestle, 33C
wrestler, 1D
wrestling, 34B
wretched, 5H
wring, 44B
wrinkle, 17I
wristwatch, 7B
wrongdoer, 9G
wrongdoing, 26A
wrought, 55B
wry, 13I

X
xylophone, 47C

Y
yacht, 11E
yak, 4E
yam, 6J
yank, 2K
yap, 19D
yearbook, 15C
yearling, 4D
yearn, 5Q
yellow jacket, 4K
yelp, 19D
yield, 10G
yip, 19D
yodel, 19C
yoga, 34D
yonder, 14K
youngster, 9D
youth, 7F
yowl, 19D
yule, 7D

Z